Local Area Networks

K C E Gee

PUBLISHED BY NCC PUBLICATIONS

British Library Cataloguing in Publication Data

Gee, K.C.E.
  Local area networks.
  1. Computer networks.
  I. Title
001.64'404   TK5105.5

ISBN 0-85012-365-8

First published in 1982 by:

NCC Publications, The National Computing Centre Limited, Oxford
Road, Manchester, M1 7ED, England.

Typeset in 10pt Times Roman by UPS Blackburn Limited,
76-80 Northgate, Blackburn, Lancashire and printed by Hobbs the
Printers of Southampton.

ISBN 0-85012-365-8

Acknowledgements

The author wishes to thank the following organisations for their literature and help in the preparation of this book:

Acorn Computers Limited
British Telecom
University of Cambridge Computer Laboratory
Central Electricity Generating Board
Computer and Systems Engineering Limited (CASE)
Datapoint (UK) Limited
The Exchange Telegraph Company
Hasler (Great Britain) Limited
Imperial Chemical Industries Limited
Institute of Electrical and Electronic Engineers (IEEE)
International Computers Limited
Joint Network Team of the Computer Board and Research Councils
Logica VTS Limited
Master Systems Limited
Network Technology Limited
Perex Limited
Racal-Milgo Limited
Rank Xerox (UK) Limited
Real Time Developments Limited
Scientific and Electronic Enterprises Limited
Sension Scientific Limited
Sintrom Electronics Limited
Tesdata Limited
Thame Systems Limited

Toltec Computer Limited
Wang (UK) Limited
Xionics Limited
Zilog (UK) Limited
Zynar Limited
3M United Kingdom Limited

The author would also like to thank the following individuals for their advice and comments on the text:

B Jackson (Hasler)
R Willson (Network Technology Limited)
P H Poole (Department of Industry)
J M Connor ⎫
J E Lane ⎬ National Computing Centre
S G Price ⎭

The Centre acknowledges with thanks the support provided by the Electronics and Avionics Requirements Board of the Department of Industry for the project from which this publication derives.

Introduction

Local area networks provide a data communications system to enable otherwise independent devices to communicate with each other. The distinguishing feature of a local area network is that the geographic area it covers is limited, often to a single office block, factory site or university campus. The data transmission rate which can be supported is often very much higher than that normally associated with data communications – up to 20 Mbps is common. The error rate is also very much lower.

Local area networks are available in a wide variety of types using a range of communications technologies and offering various levels of service. The purpose of this book is to introduce the methods used for these networks, with particular emphasis on the techniques used for systems operating today.

The book is arranged in such a manner that the reader is introduced to local area networking in stages. First local area networks are defined and distinguished from other types of network. Then their particular range of applications is discussed to show how many more things, which were uneconomic before, are possible with a cheap and reliable network.

Since local area networks use sophisticated communications techniques in a novel way, the reader is introduced to them through descriptions of the underlying principles, topologies and physical transmission media used, which are not necessarily unique to local area networks. From these, however, a new set of techniques have been developed explicitly for local area networks. The original research systems, and the current range of products which they have given rise to, are then presented in some detail, described in terms of the basic techniques explained earlier. The private on-site telephone network is an obvious candidate for organisations looking for a local network with a wide coverage. The potential for development of this system has been explored, although in the short term both are expected to develop independently in a complementary manner.

After all the current options for local area networks have been discussed, the present situation from the prospective customer's point of view is presented: namely, what standards exist, how much real live experience of these networks there is, how well they perform in practice, and how one sets about choosing one from those on the market.

Finally, the future developments are examined briefly, as well as the market for local area networks. An installation which is experimenting with the possibilities of using advanced computing and communications techniques in the office environment is described to illustrate just how important local area networks will become.

Interest in local area networks has developed very rapidly, mainly because organisations who have been considering electronic office systems have seen a need for a cheap, reliable and unobtrusive way of linking the equipment together. However, local area networks can also be valuable for distributed computing systems, internal telephone networks and possibly for transmitting visual information. They represent, therefore, a system with room for expansion.

This book is intended for designers of computing and office systems who are looking for a cost-effective way of interconnecting computer-based equipment. Individuals involved in most aspects of computing and wishing to keep abreast of developments will also find the book useful.

Contents

1   What are Local Area Networks?

INTRODUCTION

One of the great influences on the workplace and society during the second half of the 20th Century is the computer. Originally it was thought to be of use only for 'number-crunching' jobs in scientific research establishments, but very soon it was applied with outstanding success to the manipulation of business information.

In computing, the second great development has been the application of telecommunications techniques to the transport of data between remote terminals and the computer, and latterly between computers themselves. The falling cost of electronic components has led to the development of many pieces of equipment with in-built microprocessors. Such computer-controlled devices are now found in offices, factories, hospitals, schools, the home, etc. Computer-based equipment is much more flexible than hard-wired devices designed to serve the same purpose. The concept is totally different because the same computer-based device can be used for a variety of applications and modified to suit changing needs.

The widespread use, and comparative cheapness, of computer-related devices have prompted designers to look for an equally cheap means of interconnecting them so that information can be sent between them as freely as possible. The so-called *local area networks,* an example of computer communications systems, are particularly applicable to small sites such as an office block, a factory or a university campus.

There is much current interest in local area networks and new forms of local area network are coming onto the market. Many observers claim that the 'old-fashioned' networks built within a site to interconnect host computer systems and their terminals are also local area networks. However, the level of interest shown by many users in these new local area networks indicates that they, at least, can see a need for something different.

Will local area networks be as dramatic a revolution as some users expect or will they fail to live up to expectations? Whatever form they take, local area networks will be important, not least because of the cost savings they offer. It is difficult to see how the electronic revolution in the office environment can materialise without them.

LOCAL AND WIDE AREA NETWORKS

A local area network is best defined in terms of the purpose it is meant to serve rather than in terms of how it does it. A local area network is primarily a data transmission system intended to link computers and associated devices within a restricted geographical area; however, many suppliers propose to include speech in their systems. The linked computers and related equipment may be anything from full-scale mainframe computing systems to small desk-top office workstations, terminals, peripherals, etc. The key characteristic of a local area network is the fact that the whole of the network, confined to one site, is completely under the control of one organisation. This does not prevent communications taking place between users of the local area network on one site and others elsewhere. This would be achieved using wide area networks with special bridging equipment common to both the local and wide area network to perform the function of taking messages from one network and putting them on the other. Local area networks could conceivably be used as device concentrators for a wide area network.

Having decided to restrict the range of the network to within one site, various options are open to the designer. The network can have one shape (topology) among several, and many methods of transmitting the information can be used. It is unrealistic to attempt to define local area networks in terms of the topology or transmission technology as these can have much wider applicability, as will be seen. Local area networks can be used in the manner suited to the organisation which owns them, and can be completely independent of the constraints imposed by public telephone authorities, the CCITT or other public services.

Since a local area network is confined to a small area, it is possible to employ vastly different transmission methods from those commonly used on other telecommunications systems. Inexpensive line-driving equipment can be employed instead of the relatively complex modems needed for public analogue networks. High data transmission speed can be achieved by utilising the advantages of short distances and the latest electronic circuits. Thus local area networks are typified by short distances (up to 10 km, although 1 km is more usual), by a high transmission rate (0.1 to 20 Mbps), and by a low error rate. It is equally important to stress that local area networks are cheap to install and run, and provide a convenient method for interconnecting a large number of computer-based devices on a single site (eg word processors, personal computers, as well as ordinary computers).

The main attributes of present-day local area networks can be summarised:

— inexpensive transmission media;

— inexpensive devices (modems, repeaters and transceivers) to interface to the media;

— easy physical connection of devices to the media;

— high data transmission rates;

— network data transmission rate independent of the rates used by the attached devices, making it easier for devices of one speed to send information to devices of another speed;

— a high degree of interconnection between devices;

— every attached device having the potential to communicate with every other device on the network;

— there is seldom a central controlling processor which polls the attached devices on the network;

— in the majority of cases, each attached device hears (but does not process) messages intended for other devices as well as for itself.

It is important to note that neither the actual data transmission rate used, the access method nor the topology of the network are essential characteristics.

As local area networks have developed so it has become clearer what equipment will use them and what applications will be supported. Although some forms of local area network can be extended to analogue voice equipment (eg the telephone) or to video devices, most are primarily suited to devices generating digital data streams at a moderate rate (reference 1.1):

— computers (minis, micros, and mainframes);

— computer terminals, both dumb and intelligent;

— personal computer systems based on microprocessors;

— office workstations;

— mass storage devices;

— printers and plotters;

— file servers;

— photo- and telecopiers;

— process monitoring and control equipment;

— bridges and gateways to other networks.

The most relevant applications are:

— file transfer and access;

— word and text processing;

— electronic message handling;

— personal filing and information handling;

— graphical information;

— remote database access;

— personal computing;

— digital voice transmission and storage.

Special types of local area networks have been developed to link mainframe computer systems which are too far apart to use normal direct wiring, or which are from different suppliers and thus employ different interfaces.

Wide area networks include all the networks which are involved in transporting information from one geographic location to another. The scale is much greater than in local networks. A wide area network will almost always be employed whenever the information in electronic form on cables leaves the site, even if it is only to cross over the street to another building.

Whenever one thinks of a data communications network, one is normally thinking of a wide area network. The data transmission rates involved are generally between a few hundred and a few thousand bits per second, with the usual maximum of about 50 kbps. The distances involved will be from around 1 km to possibly thousands of kilometres. The error rate will be far from negligible and error detection procedures are essential for practically every situation.

Possibly one of the most significant aspects of a wide area network when comparing it with the freedom of a local area network, is the involvement of a public telecommunications authority. Regardless of whether the network is made up from private circuits, uses the public telephone network or a special-purpose data transmission system, the controlling authority is almost always the public authority. In order to protect their equipment and employees, the authority lays down rules which must be observed by anyone connecting to their lines. In most countries, stringent requirements are also imposed on the characteristics of the data transmissions.

OTHER SHORT-DISTANCE NETWORKS

Typical on-site computer networks are based on point-to-point direct wiring between the devices. If the device is a simple terminal, only one circuit is supported – between the terminal and the terminal controller or the computer it serves. Computers are usually capable of supporting several circuits to different points at the same time. These may be to terminals, controllers and also other computer systems. The result in a typical distributed system supporting a few computer systems and many terminals is a mass of cables interconnecting all the devices. Even then there is no guarantee that a terminal attached to one system will be able to converse with one of the other computers or with another terminal. Although a local area network cannot guarantee that all devices connected to it will be able to work together, it would provide the opportunity for complete interconnection using simple software and possibly even a single cable. Using standard computer networking techniques, this would often involve considerable extra wiring and special software in the nodes of the network to route messages intended for other destinations.

The on-site communications networks usually encountered are those between computer processors and their peripheral devices such as disk stores, printers and communication controllers. These circuits all exhibit very high data transmission rates and few errors, but can only operate over very short distances (up to a few metres). All the devices on these networks are closely knit together, and the times when they can transmit and receive are governed by strict rules laid down by the designer of the system and usually under the control of the central processor. Naturally a network of this type does not allow free interconnection and message transmission between all types of device within a typical office or factory. Thus they cannot be considered to be local area networks.

The distinction between on-site circuit and packet switched networks and local area networks is not so clear. A circuit switched system is typified by the telephone system. One device wishing to contact another device does so by means of a series of links which together form a complete circuit. The linking is effected by one or more exchanges. A packet switched system operates in a completely different manner. Messages, or parts of messages, are placed in packets which include the network address of the destination. Devices/exchanges on the network take each packet and transport it to its destination. There is no reason why a local area network, which generally falls within the broad characteristics outlined in the previous section, could not be constructed using a star-shaped network with a central system performing circuit, message or packet switching functions. There should be no significant restriction imposed on the data transmission rate, nor, using the latest digital techniques, on the speed of switching between lines.

HISTORY

The history of local area networks has involved bringing together many separate developments. By the early 1970s some experimental work had been done on networks specifically designed to carry digital information. Until that time most computer networks had been built around traditional telecommunications systems designed to transport analogue speech signals. Digital information was translated into an analogue stream of tones which represented the bit pattern being transmitted. The various analogue signals were re-translated by the recipient back into the corresponding digital information.

The transmission of computer-related information requires that some of the transmitted information relates to the control of the devices involved. Take for example a simple terminal. Early techniques were built around a repertoire of characters, each represented by 5, 6 or 7 bits. Some of these characters were used to represent normal alphabetic and numeric characters, and other information used in written text and mathematics. Other characters were used specifically to control the terminal and to delimit the information flow. The terminal, for example, needed permission from its controller before it could transmit. It also had to be told when to move to the next line, skip lines and so on. These are the control characters: the more sophisticated the terminal, the more control characters needed.

Because early computing devices were often based on electromechanical components, the speed at which they could send and receive data streams was very limited: each character had to be delimited to prevent the sender and receiver getting out of step. After some improvements had been made to these character-by-character data transmission techniques, a completely new method was devised.

In this, the digital information stream was split up into blocks and enclosed within special control characters or fields. The length of the blocks could vary, and the start and end of each block would be flagged by special sequences of bits. Between the control fields, the pattern of the bits could include characters which would otherwise be control characters, but the sending and receiving devices would ignore them.

Blocking removed many of the restrictions imposed on users of the earlier character-oriented techniques. It meant, for instance, that a computer could send an image of the bit representations of information exactly as held inside the store. Before blocks were used, these bit representations would almost certainly have contained sequences which would be interpreted as control characters, with rather unexpected results. The technique employed to overcome these restrictions was to convert the information into normal text and transmit this. It was usually extremely wasteful of time and communications capacity (eg a decimal number could be stored in six characters in computer code, but may require more than double this number of characters to represent it as a string of decimal digits).

Once the idea of putting data into blocks for transmission was accepted, the technique was expanded to provide other facilities. The most important in the present context was to use one of the control fields as the address of the source or destination. The now familiar technique of packet switching for data transmission employs fields containing both addresses. If each block of data contained the address, then more than one pair of devices could share the same circuits. A block of data with another destination address could be ignored by the other devices.

Packet switching is one of the key influences on the design of current local area networks, since this is a method by which a single transmission system is able to be shared. (Packet switching is too complex a topic to be covered in detail here. Interested readers are directed to reference 1.2.)

Packet switching networks are ideal for long-distance, high-performance data networks carrying frequent but short-duration traffic because the long-distance circuits can be of very high quality and have a wide bandwidth, since their capacity and cost will be shared amongst many users. Each packet is placed on the network by the sender and the network uses the destination address field to route it through the network interleaved with packets from several other users.

The University of Hawaii adapted packet switching in a novel way to suit its particular requirements. The geographic problems of the Hawaiian Islands, and the lack of very reliable telephone circuits, forced the University into finding a new way for the computer terminals on the outlying islands to communicate with the computer centre. They decided to use a radio broadcasting system. The usual packet switching system employs special controlling nodes in the network itself to interleave one packet with another and perform the routeing functions. In a radio broadcasting system this is not possible, so in the Hawaiian system, called ALOHA, every device just broadcast a packet of information whenever it had one ready. All the devices continuously listened to the radio channel and read into storage packets addressed to them. They acknowledged receipt by sending back another packet. Full details of ALOHA are given later in the book.

The significance of ALOHA lay in its use of a shared medium in which there was no direct control over who transmitted packets. This system was a major influence on the designers of contention bus systems typified by Ethernet, also discussed in later chapters.

The packet technique was also adopted by designers of other local area networks. The ring systems, which constitute the other main technique, leave the packet interleaving and routeing to all the devices on the ring. The packets are transmitted only when the node has permission. The ways that this permission can be given vary from one system to another.

Another major development which has made modern local area networks possible is the availability of high-speed electronic components at a reasonable price. Computers normally employ what are known as buses for communications between the separate circuits which go to make up the complete machine: the processor, the storage, the input/output ports, etc. The bus may be used for many purposes, and seldom does one join just two components unless information passes along it almost continuously. Buses are usually shared communications channels. By extending the bus ideas beyond the computer, and by employing simple signalling and transmission techniques, a limited-distance communications network for interconnecting several pieces of equipment is possible at low cost.

By bringing together the packet format for the data and the shared cheap high-speed bus ideas from computer hardware, local area networks became a real possibility. The need for low-cost, short-distance communications facilities has arisen in parallel with the development of individual low-cost computers and workstations. Hence local area networks have found a ready market.

Both the techniques used in local area networks were developed for completely different purposes. Packet switching was designed for long-distance shared networks. Buses were used for very short distance communications where very high speed was all important. Combining the two has yielded a network for medium-distance shared networks operating at fairly high speed.

THE SCOPE OF LOCAL AREA NETWORKS

Unlike most telecommunications networking technologies, local area networks were developed by the computing community to fill the need for a communications technique which provided transmission speeds and error rates comparable with those experienced in computers. Existing telecommunications methods (ie analogue and public) are generally much slower and exhibit a high error rate. Distributed computing systems require that computers as well as terminals are involved in sending and receiving data. A slow-speed, error-prone network is of little value when thousands or millions of bits are being sent from one computer to another. A network which is adequate for interactions between terminals and computer systems may be practically useless for a more demanding role.

Most local area networks in research environments were established to serve specific computing requirements, either for interconnecting computers in a distributed processing system or for serving the needs of an electronic office. One notable exception was the network built by the Swiss telecommunications company Hasler to investigate the potential of a shared network for interconnecting digital telephones on a single site. It was the early success of this system which prompted some research into ring networks for data transmission.

Research networks demonstrated that high-quality networks could be built cheaply when confined to a limited area, but it was the rapid development of microprocessors and their introduction into every conceivable device which prompted the rapid exploitation of local area networks. Having put a microprocessor into a teminal or a typewriter at low cost, so making it in effect a personal computer, the data transmission requirements of that device may become more demanding. The appeal of a personal intelligent workstation communicating with other workstations and computer systems is somewhat lessened if the cost of connecting it to a network is going to exceed the cost of the device itself. Hence the interest in local networks which offer the low-cost solution to local communications.

However, local area networks are unlikely to exist in isolation. It is unrealistic to expect that a set of workstations or computers on one local network will never need to communicate with devices on other networks. Although local area networks are aimed specifically at servicing the needs of the users of that network, provision will be made in practice to allow one local network to talk to other networks, possibly through public networks (telephone, private or public data networks) in between.

In this manner, local area networks will offer their users the ability to access other computer services provided either by their own computers, by other companies, or by other local area networks elsewhere. This is one of the ideas underlying Project Universe.

Project Universe is an experimental network in the UK involving representatives of the universities, telecommunications equipment suppliers and the software industry in the use of a satellite to interconnect several otherwise autonomous local area networks around the country.

Most of these local networks are Cambridge Ring systems, but other types can be used, if available. Satellite networks share some features with local area networks, as can be readily appreciated when considering the influence ALOHA has had on local area network designs. In both systems all devices can hear all transmissions. But the transmission times involved when using satellites are very significant due to the distance over which the signals must travel: ie to the satellite and back. This delay has enormous effects on the transmission protocols which are used. Even when satellites are being used for exclusive point-to-point transmissions in which no-one else is sharing the channel, special protocols need to be employed to prevent wastage of transmission capacity. When the channel is shared amongst a large number of users, the problems are compounded. To investigate possible solutions to these problems is the main reason for Project Universe.

When one network is connected to another network, special bridging devices called gateways are needed to convert transmissions from one set of procedures, speeds, etc, to the other. Project Universe will employ gateways on each of the local area networks involved. But gateway design is not confined to the particular needs of satellite networks, although these do pose extra problems.

Broadcast satellite networks are also more difficult to design in a manner which ensures that all the users have an equal share. The ALOHA network experienced this problem and tried many solutions. Provided that the number of users accessing the network at any time is reasonably small, little information is lost in transit, necessitating retransmission. Project Universe will examine ways of allocating the bandwidth fairly amongst all its users.

To summarise, local area networks are a significant improvement over the older telecommunications techniques employed for computers. At present, the high-speed cheap and reliable local network confines communications to one small area, but with suitable use of wide area networks and gateways between them, local area networks could be linked together. Although current products do not provide complete freedom in the choice of devices which can be used on the network (due to lack of interfacing hardware suitable for every computer-related device on the market), the prospects for interconnection are good. Local area networks can provide the basis for many services which will enhance the work of the office employee. In particular, access to information databases and the provision of information-handling and messaging routines will be available.

2   Application Areas

INTRODUCTION

There are many types of local area networks, some with a wide range of facilities, but the basic purpose of them all is to provide a communication channel between computer-related devices. Some of the products marketed as local area networks have provided, in addition to the communications facilities, an integrated set of services which are applicable to office environments. Others concentrate on the communications aspects which the user can utilise as necessary, and on to which the services the applications require can be put. These two aspects of local area networks reflect, to a large extent, the different environments in which they have grown: the office products market for the integrated network which provides many services; and the computer or data processing market for the basic data communications network.

Practically all the devices which will use a local area network will be based on, or related to, a computer processor. These may be traditional computer systems which have a powerful processor supported by on-line storage media and input and output devices. They can also be minicomputers, microcomputers, terminals (both intelligent and dumb), peripheral devices, electronic office products such as word processors, and all manner of equipment which incorporates microprocessors. The amount of equipment which fits the description is already very wide, and is increasing very rapidly. The one common feature of the equipment which is applicable for use with local area networks is that all the devices are able to communicate with others on the same network.

Since much of the business information produced travels between users and devices on the same site, it can be argued that a low-cost local area network linking everybody together should have considerable appeal.

Having widespread interconnection of devices gives the users and designers of the network the potential to do many things which would be difficult or impossible any other way. For example, in a network for distributed processing there is often a need for back-up in case one of the processors fails, or a link between them becomes unusable. Local networks give their users easier access to a wider range of facilities and services, such as shared storage, shared computer power, etc. New applications can be developed, such as electronic mail, which really demands a large number of users all on the same network.

Users of older computer systems benefit from on-line access from terminals. Users of distributed processing networks benefit from sharing resources such as expensive peripherals, and by allowing terminal access to several different computer systems. Local area networks made the interconnection of computer-based devices easier to achieve.

Electronic office systems are being developed in which many workers will have ready access to a workstation which can perform many routine office functions. Linking the workstations has many immediate advantages since much of an office worker's time is spent sending, receiving and dealing with information. It will soon be possible to integrate data with voice and video traffic on local networks, so opening up a wide range of new opportunities.

Will the mere existence of local area networks bring about changes in the way people and systems work, or should local area networks be tailored to the work now being done? The answer probably is that both are true. To take the railways as an analogy, they were built for a specific purpose: to move materials needed by industry from their source to the factory, and to move the finished goods to the place where they would be used. But the very existence of a quick method of transport brought about enormous changes in society. No longer did people need to live within walking distance of their place of work. Nor did factories need to be placed where the raw materials and workers were at hand. People could actually travel long distances from their homes to have a holiday, which in its turn brought about a whole new industry, the leisure industry. Once local area networks are installed, it is conceivable that they will bring about new work patterns within the office and factory. It is doubtful that a new method of working would be thought out and then a local area network installed to serve it.

Local area networks can be justified in terms of their existing uses. The

technology also exists to develop them to handle voice and visual information as well as data. In many cases the cost of the network could be
justified for any of these on their own. In this chapter, we will look at
some of the known areas of use for local area networks (computer and
terminal networks and the electronic office) and speculate on some of the
areas which could be developed once the communications infrastructure
exists.

COMPUTER NETWORKS

A computer network is an arrangement of computer systems and the
facilities needed to access them and store information. The various elements are linked by some means, usually telecommunications circuits.
Processing of user applications may be performed at several places in the
network, in which case it is often referred to as a distributed computing
system. Alternatively, the network may exist to allow users over a wide
area to access a central computing system by means of various types of
terminals. The network in the latter case may contain some processors
but these will perform functions associated with data transmission and
not with application processing of user-supplied information. The particular requirement of terminal networks from the point of view of a local
area network is considered later in this chapter.

Many computer networks extend over several sites which are linked by
the public telephone network or by circuits which are leased from the
public authority. Collectively these networks are called *Wide Area Networks*. The user of them must conform to the standards for connection
and use laid down by the supplying authority. Local area networks can
only be used to link equipment which is contained wholly on one site and
which does not require that the public authority, or anyone else, be
involved. To make the maximum use of local area networks in situations
where the complete computer network also extends over more than one
site, or where access from the outside world is needed, provision must be
made for linking local networks with normal computer or wide area
networks. This is usually accomplished by means of special computers,
called *gateways,* which perform protocol and speed conversion and which
act as an interface between networks.

Computer networks come in a variety of forms, each one having been
built to serve the needs of the organisation to which they belong. Some
organisations want a main central computing and storage facility which

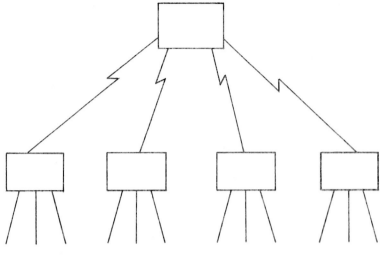

End-users or other computer systems

Figure 2.1   Hierarchy of Star Networks

controls all the rest of the equipment in the network. The outlying computers exist to serve the central system although they may perform some processing themselves which would be inappropriate or inefficient to be performed centrally.

Other organisations have placed the responsibility for running applications with the departments which generate or use the data: here, central responsibility is retained only for program and system writing and maintenance. In other cases the need to have computing capacity always available is so crucial to the organisation that the network has been designed to provide a degree of back-up in case of processor and telecommunications link failures.

Some applications, notably in the industrial production area, require many computers to cooperate to perform a task. Computers which monitor and control production processes in a factory often fall into this category: the failure of one part of the production process will affect both those processes which supply the materials to the failed process, and which use the products of it. To respond quickly enough, and to provide back-up computing power in case a control computer fails, often requires that the computers are linked.

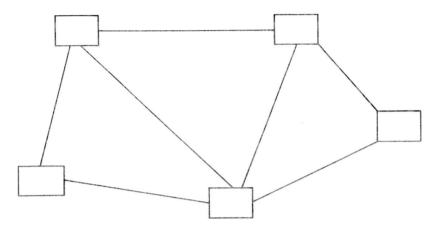

Figure 2.2   Mesh Network

To meet these many and varied requirements, computer networks have developed in a number of ways. The topology is the most obvious variable. A centrally-based network, with links to devices feeding it with information and allowing users to access the results, is generally based on a star-shaped system. Most commonly the network is in fact a hierarchy of stars, as shown in Figure 2.1.

Other network topologies frequently encountered are the mesh network (Figure 2.2), in which a number of nodes are connected together but information from one sometimes has to pass via a third party to reach its destination because no direct link exists; and the fully-interconnected network (Figure 2.3), in which each node is directly connected to every other one. Less commonly found at present, but likely to become more important in the context of local area networks, are the bus, illustrated in Figure 2.4, and the ring or loop, shown in Figure 2.5.

To service the different network topologies and different requirements of the users, the manufacturers and suppliers of networking products have produced various facilities, some of which are:

— *Multiple routeing*. Information from one device to another in the network may not always need to follow the same route. Two different schemes have evolved. One is *alternative routeing* in which information normally follows one route between any two nodes, but it can be made to take another if the network or link

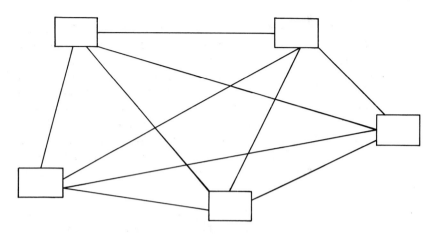

Figure 2.3   Fully-Interconnected Network

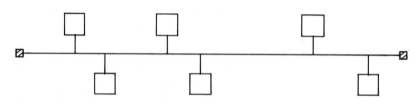

Figure 2.4   Bus (or Highway)

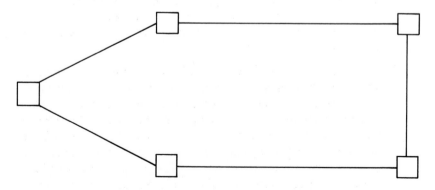

Figure 2.5   Ring or Loop Network

fails, or is overloaded, or the network supervisor decides to alter the traffic flow for some reason. The other system is *adaptive routeing*. With this technique the network as a whole keeps track of the state of traffic on each link and decides at the time of transmission of a message, or any separate part of it, which route it should use at that time. Thus a message which is split into three blocks for transmission may reach its destination by three different routes. Such a system enables the network to function without attention even when links or nodes fail. The system of alternative routeing described earlier, requires some outside intervention to change the routes.

— *Remote Access.* A vital element in the success of most networks is for a terminal or computer system in one location to be able to access and work with another system on another part of the network as they would if they were local to each other. This requires that all intermediate nodes are transparent to the users. Application programs, computer systems, files, databases and peripherals should all be accessible remotely; most network suppliers go some way towards this.

— *File Transfer.* In systems where several computers are linked it is often advantageous to transfer all or part of a file from one system to another so that it can be accessed or updated locally rather than remotely. Moving files can be difficult if the source and target systems are not matched. However, the requirement is considered to be so important that the problem of file transfer is addressed by many suppliers. In addition to moving files, users sometimes want to manipulate (update, delete, copy, archive, etc) them from a remote location. This can pose similar problems to transferring them.

— *Job Transfer and Manipulation.* Users of mainframe computer systems often use a special terminal to enter a job in one place to be run on the computer in another location. The requirement is even more urgent for distributed processing systems because one computer on the system may itself transfer a job to another if the alternative computer is better able to process it. Having moved a job to another location, the system must permit access to all the files it requires, regardless of their location, and the operator or user must still be able to control its execution. The output should also be produced in the correct location.

— *Resource Sharing*. Networks based on minicomputers often grew up because of the need to share relatively expensive peripherals and storage systems amongst all the computers on the network. Frequently only one or two high-speed printers and hard-disk files were provided for a number of computers. With the introduction of cheap microcomputers in large numbers into the office environment, this requirement is even more acute. Here it makes a lot of sense to share a high capacity hard-disk unit, rather than each system being supplied with low-speed, low-capacity floppy disks.

— *Database Access*. An organisation which uses a corporate database needs a network which is capable of providing users with access to that database. Some organisations may profit by parts of the database being kept or updated in different locations whilst still retaining the overall unity of structure. The problems of distributed databases are still subjects for research and a common solution now is to locate the whole database is one place but permit access to it from all over the network.

The above are just some of the services which are provided for normal computer networks of today. The way local area networks fit into this background will now be discussed.

A significant feature of the more traditional computer system is the rather slow data transfer rate which is supported. A rate of a few thousand bits per second can severely hamper data transfer between computers although it may be more than adequate for terminal transactions. Linking computers by circuits which operate at speeds significantly lower than the computers' ordinary operating speeds can cause difficulties unless the computer systems themselves have made special provision for such links in the form of communications hardware and software.

It was against this background that some local area network technologies were developed, notably the Cambridge Ring, designed for use within the University of Cambridge Computer Laboratory. The ring was designed to link several different computers and terminals in order that the equipment and files could be shared amongst all the users. At the same time it was to provide the communications subnetwork to help with research into distributed systems.

The Cambridge Ring was designed to operate at speeds comparable

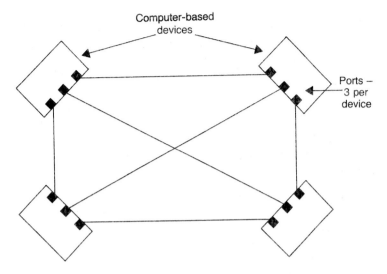

a) Fully-Interconnected Using Separate Ports and Links

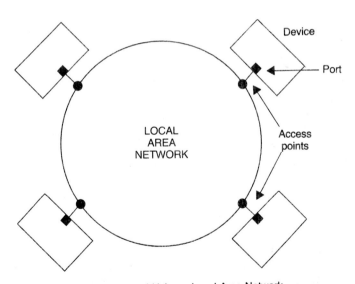

b) Fully-Interconnected Using a Local Area Network

Figure 2.6   Alternative Methods of Constructing a Fully-Interconnected Network

with the internal computing speeds of the machines on the network. 10 Mbps was chosen as the raw transmission speed which gives in practice a point-to-point transfer rate of over 1 Mbps because of the way the network is accessed and shared. The ring is simple in concept and easy to implement in practice, and it affords a convenient and cheap method of interconnecting all the devices. Terminals can thus access all the computers using the same wires, rather than a separate link to each being needed.

Since its installation in the mid-1970s, the Cambridge Ring has proved ideal for its purpose. It shows that a very useful distributed system which looks like a fully interconnected network to the user can be constructed and operated easily.

In a normal fully-interconnected network each node requires (n-1) links and ports, if n is the total number of devices (see Figure 2.6). In the usual local area network, only one port is required to connect to the network interface device or repeater, which are the devices responsible for sending and receiving information to and from the network.

In common with most other forms of local area network, the Cambridge Ring removes the problem of having to control several input/ output ports at each node whilst still enabling information to be sent to any other node without the need to pass through intermediate computers.

A more common situation is illustrated in Figure 2.7. Here three computers serve a number of terminals. These terminals are connected to their local computer systems, through which they can access other systems and the shared resources located on system P3. Schematically the network is shown in Figure 2.7a. In practice the system would be wired up something like that shown in Figure 2.7b where terminals in the office have individual links to the computers. Installing a local area network using the corridor as the route for the wire, we can get the simple situation shown at Figure 2.7c. The multiplexer used for the terminals in the big office can be dispensed with as well as simplifying the wiring in the rest of the system.

Once the basic local area network is installed, new services and features can be added to enhance the system for the user since many of the interconnection restrictions can be removed. Typically, a mailbox and shared file facilities can be provided and, if the interface units can be suitably designed, protocol and code conversions may be provided to enable otherwise incompatible devices to work together.

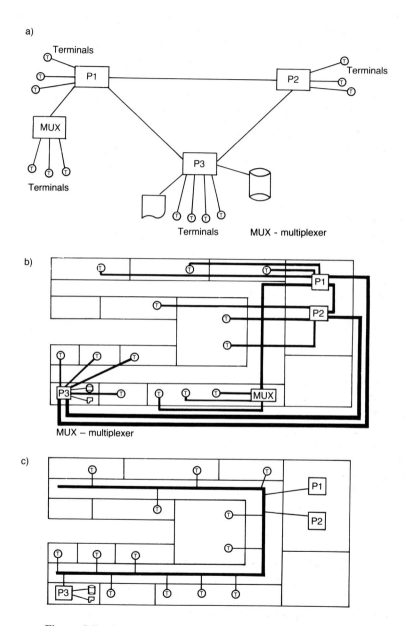

Figure 2.7 Computer Network in Office Environment

Thus, we can see that local area networks can provide significant advantages for computer networks when these are wholly within one site. If the networks cover several sites, the provision of a gateway device to interface between the local area network and the wide area network is essential. Where the network incorporates a computer system which is capable of interfacing to wide area networks, this system itself could be made to perform as a gateway.

TERMINAL NETWORKS

The bulk of terminals in use are still unintelligent devices and require terminal controllers or specialised circuits in computers to control them. The networks which serve these terminals are essentially stars, possibly multiple stars or hierarchies. In the centre is the computer system which includes most, if not all, of the computing resources, data storage, printers and other peripherals associated with serving the end-user. A typical example is shown in Figure 2.8.

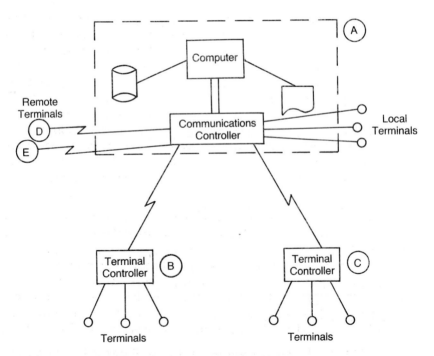

Figure 2.8   Typical Terminal Network

The processing unit is connected through a communications controller to the terminals. Sometimes terminals are connected directly to the computer, although these are usually restricted to those with special control or speed requirements, such as raster graphics terminals. Remote terminals are generally connected through public or private lines or a data transmission network to the communications controller. These generally operate at a low speed because of restrictions imposed by the line quality. Local terminals can use different techniques and transmission facilities which, combined with the limited distance over which they operate, mean that higher data transmission rates can be supported.

Where clusters of terminals exist in a remote location, it is common to connect them to the central system through a terminal controller which is local to them. The terminal controller can often be connected to the communications controller through relatively high-speed lines of good quality. The terminal controller performs the dual purpose of handling the terminals, which are usually unintelligent, and sharing the high-speed line capacity amongst them.

It was from this type of system that the early distributed computing systems developed. The remote terminal controllers are capable of performing end-user applications themselves and this can very significantly reduce the load imposed on the links to the central system. Reduced transmission load means that poorer quality, and hence much cheaper, circuits could be used, more than saving the cost of the extra intelligence required. In the early systems, the terminal controllers performed simple user-related tasks, such as data format checking. Their capabilities soon increased with the advent of cheaper processors and on-line storage. Thus the terminal controller was able to perform many of the data editing and even some full-scale applications itself, with minimum reference to the central system.

How can the basic form of a computer network be adapted for use with local area networks? The first thing to realise is that the network shown in Figure 2.8 is in fact, when considered in the light of local areas, three interconnected networks: one network at each of the locations A, B and C. The remote terminals represented at the separate locations D and E are outside each of the other local systems and cannot sensibly be incorporated in any local area network. Thus, the network can be redrawn as in Figure 2.9 to show how local area networks could be incorporated.

Notice that the communications and terminal controllers have gone

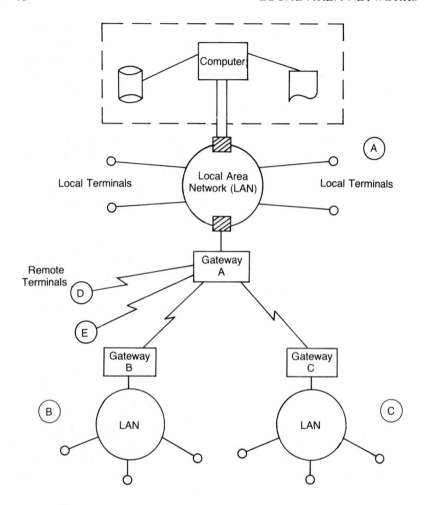

Figure 2.9   Terminal Network using Local Area Networks

and have been replaced by gateway devices. These gateways are devices common to both the local area networks and the public networks, or wide area networks made up from circuits leased from the public telecommunications authority. The function of the gateway is to provide facilities to convert between the procedures used in the local network and those required by the public authority.

Although the solution just described is possible, it is unusual at this

time to put local area networks at locations B and C if there is no
processing capacity there as well. It is more common to leave these as a
terminal controller based system with links to the central site. A local area
network on the central site A is much more likely. Gateway A may then
be a terminal controller with a direct connection to the computer system
and a connection to the local area network. The form of the local area
network at site A depends on the characteristics of the devices. If the
terminals are capable of operating as loop devices, and if the controller
could be a loop controller, then it is feasible to construct the local area
network as a loop. If the terminals are intelligent, or if there are
microprocessor-based devices which are to be connected into the network, a loop system based on the communications controller is not such a
good solution. It would be better under those circumstances to install ring
or bus local area networks.

Local area networks are really best suited for terminal networks when
there are a large number of terminals on one site. The capacity inherent in
most local area networks makes them suitable for handling all the traffic
which can be generated, even when the terminals have to be polled by the
controller.

THE ELECTRONIC OFFICE

The introduction of computing capacity into the office environment, and
the incorporation of microprocessors into typewriters and other standard
office machines, has far more repercussions than this book could possibly
hope to cover. (The interested reader is referred in the first instance to
reference 2.1 for more information on the electronic office.) A brief
description of normal office functions and the influence of the electronic
office is presented here. Various normal office functions can be identified:

— *document preparation:* typing, updating and correcting documents, including taking dictation and copying the final results;

— *message distribution:* telephoning, mail and travel to and from
   meetings;

— *personal information management:* use of filing cabinets, in/out
   trays, diaries and planning charts;

— *information access:* reference to corporate information, reference
   documents, library, bibliographic services, etc.

The emerging office technology aims to use the advantages in electronics, computing and communications technologies to make the above tasks easier to perform, and to be carried out more efficiently. Information in the electronic office should be easier to access, giving the worker more information which is more up-to-date. This can be done more quickly than with a manual system. People should also be more accessible by means of an electronic messaging system: if the recipient of a message is absent or unavailable, the message can wait in his electronic 'in-tray'. Files can be shared, making it much easier for two or more people to work on one document and removing the requirement to duplicate documents.

Electronic office systems are intended to help the individual with the normal filing and retrieval tasks associated with office work. Documents should be easy to retrieve from the electronic 'filing cabinet' and there should be no possibility of a document being replaced in the wrong section – a major cause of lost time with manual systems.

Above all, the electronic office should free the worker from many of the mundane administrative support tasks. The released time can then be spent more profitably on the major job.

The main components of the electronic office are:

— *The workstation:* a device for accessing and using the files and services provided. It is suitable for both experienced and naive users and is similar in appearance to the normal computer VDU terminal but should have local processing power and access to a printer and personal file storage. Preferably the keyboard should be suitable for text handling rather than program and data input. One workstation for each user is the ideal.

— *Shared facilities:* facilities which are expensive to buy or which any one user does not use continuously. A high-speed printer, a good quality printer, data processing facilities are examples of facilities which are needed only occasionally for a single user, but which are usually required at some time. High-speed disk storage, archiving facilities and service programs are examples of facilities which are needed by all users but which are expensive to provide on an individual basis.

— *Access to external facilities:* the normal office worker does not work in a vacuum and needs to communicate in various ways with the outside world. To do this, there is a need for access to specialised services and databases, information services, libraries, patents information, data networks and possibly electronic mail services. These should be accessible from the office worker's desk.

— *Communications facilities:* to link the workstation to the above services and other workstations. The ways this can be achieved include a central computer system with links to all the workstations and services, a central switch similar to a telephone exchange which will provide the links between the workstation and the service the user requests, or a local area network. The telephone is also an important element for communications and this may be integrated with the data handling functions. The communications facilities should be easy to connect to, easy to add new devices to, and be high-speed.

The current thrust in the electronic office is in the document preparation area (word processing). This is because it is a straightforward extension of the current practice of typing and document correction. It is fairly cheap to introduce word processors to the office and the users require relatively little extra training to be able to use them. The results are easily assessed and experience has shown that word processing increases both productivity and document quality.

Word processors can be stand-alone devices but some extra benefits can be obtained if the system is shared. Better text handling facilities can be provided by a minicomputer-based word processor system than can be possible with a small stand-alone machine. The central storage of information makes it easier to control, with text being accessible to more than one user. One person can type the initial document from handwritten script or dictation, and the originator can modify it from another location. The disadvantage of the shared approach is that all the word processors may cease working if the central device fails.

Apart from word processing, other services should be available in the electronic office; for example:

— *Telex and Teletex:* external national and international electronic mail services using either a dedicated network in the case of Telex, or various networks in the case of Teletex services;

— *Facsimile:* electronic transmission of images which typically are not text, such as pictures, drawings, annotated documents, etc;

— *Information:* corporate and external reference files and databases as well as personal information;

— *Electronic messages:* memos between workers on one site take up a significant amount of time. Sending electronic memos from one workstation to another can be quicker than any other method. There is also the saving in paper and in methods of storing paper messages to be taken into consideration;

— *Conferencing:* there are many forms of conferencing including voice (provided by some private telephone exchanges), computer conferencing and various levels of video conferencing;

— *Voice:* voice messages will obviously remain a major means of communication, even in the electronic office, but another technique which holds promise is voice annotation (comments, alterations, etc) to text;

— *Data processing:* ready access to data processing facilities and to the files and services available on the company's computer system should be available;

— *Computation services:* computing facilities local to the workstation, and access to central and external computer services ranging from simple programming to complex applications-oriented systems (eg modelling).

Local area networks, in one form or another, are a vital element in linking together the components of the electronic office. In particular they are essential to provide the user at a workstation with access to all the other workstations and services which can be provided in a shared-resource system. Local area networks can provide the catalyst to the integration of the different services and the media for communication (voice, data, text, visual, facsimile).

In addition, the problem of linking very large numbers of workstations and other office machinery together demands that a fresh look is taken at communications between computer-related devices. This was one of the forces behind the development of the Ethernet local area network. Ethernet was studied by the Xerox Corporation in the USA as a method of linking office workstations and providing them with access to expensive resources such as copiers, printers and computers. The concept of Ethernet is simple: provide a single data highway to which a very large number of devices can be attached, all of which can then address each other. The concept has proved so successful that a large number of Ethernet systems are now installed.

A local area network for the office environment should permit a large number of users to be connected to it, and should be capable of supporting a wide range of equipment. The cost of connecting each device to the network must be low compared with the cost of each device.

Ideally the local area network should be capable of transmitting information in a variety of forms: analogue voice, digitised voice, data, text, video (colour and black and white). The different information types demand different network responses since some types of information, real-time colour video, for example, cannot afford to wait for a convenient place to transmit, otherwise the picture judders and voice conversations become difficult to follow.

In the office environment, the provision of user-oriented services by the network is very important. Electronic mailing within the office or site is something which should be provided as part of the network rather than provided by a separate computer-based device which the other users can access. Similarly, traffic and usage statistics should be gathered by the network for performance and usage monitoring.

At the time of writing, local area network products can only go part of the way towards meeting the demands of the electronic office. Without the basic communications facilities provided by the local network it is unlikely that office automation could proceed much beyond the word processor systems which have been available for some time. In the next section the advanced facilities of the electronic office are considered in more detail with particular reference to their impact on the design of local area networks.

NEW APPLICATIONS

New applications are coming along which would be difficult or expensive to implement without local area networks. In this section the most important ones at the present time will be examined, together with the ways local area networks can be used to implement the systems. Where relevant, the possibilities for these applications without local area networks will also be discussed.

Electronic Message Systems

Most electronic message systems are set up to transfer messages easily and quickly between members of a group of users. To achieve this in a sensible manner, a range of facilities are needed:

— write and edit messages;

— send messages to one person or a group;

— store the messages sent and received;

— answer a message which has been received;

— request a reply from someone after a message has been sent;

— confirmation of delivery;

— provide adequate message privacy;

— be able to set an urgent message priority.

To make an electronic mail system work effectively, each user in the group needs to have a workstation available, and all the workstations must be interconnected. The network must also include a device which can control the message system by deciding which routes to use, etc. Preferably there should be a central filing system which is used to store the messages.

Since for certain types of organisation (typically medium to large headquarters sites), much of this type of messaging is within a local group on a single site, a local area network is the obvious choice for interconnecting the devices. The network must provide full interconnectability between all the workstations and the message-handling system. The speed at which the network can operate is not critical, but it is more important that the network is reliable and always available when needed.

An electronic mail system can easily be constructed without using a local area network by installing a central mail server which performs the message store and forwarding. Adding new workstations to a star system of this character is not always easy and there may be a relatively low limit on the number of users permitted. Newer computerised private telephone exchanges may be suitable in this role.

Using a local area network based on a ring or bus generally offers some advantages. Typically, new workstations can be added without much trouble wherever they are required (provided, of course, that the network is accessible from that location). Large numbers of workstations are easily supported on most local area network systems and the initial installation is usually quite cheap.

In situations where there is a need to send and receive messages electronically to and from other sites, the local area network must be equipped with a gateway device for the public system.

Information Management

Information management is associated with handling and accessing both corporate and personal information. By corporate information is meant data which is used by the organisation as a whole. It can cover information related to the trading performance of the organisation, and reference data needed by individuals to carry out their work (catalogues, directories, data sheets, timetables, library services, etc). Personal information is that information required by an individual to organise work schedules effectively. For example, diary details, details of meetings, lists of names, addresses and telephone numbers, are all types of personal information without which the average office worker would find it difficult to work efficiently.

Many organisations are now considering how the electronic workstation can be used to provide the information handling required by managers and professionals. Naturally, each workstation must be able to access relevant corporate and personal information. The worker, of course, should be positively excluded from accessing company confidential files or information personal to other members of the organisation, unless explicit permission is granted.

Corporate information will invariably be held on central storage devices, often associated with the company's computer system. Personal information could be stored on personal floppy disks, although this is generally not the most convenient method. A better system is to set up a specialised file handling system on the network, which is shared by every user, but which has the necessary security locks to prevent unauthorised access to another user's data.

To meet both the corporate and personal information handling requirements, each workstation must be on a network which includes the appropriate databases and files. The network should be highly reliable, especially in circumstances where no paper copy of the information is easily accessible in case of failure of the network. Local area networks are particularly suited to the handling of personal information where all the users share a high-speed, high-capacity data storage device. This has very obvious advantages when more than one person is associated with handling a piece of information, such as writing a report. By using the same shared-file storage system, all the users involved can access the same version without separate copies having to be made.

Accessing a corporate database, where this is stored on a company computer system, is also possible with a local area network, provided the computer system itself can be connected to the network. Accessing database and information services which are outside the organisation can pose more problems. Typically, examples of these services would be science and business information, bibliographic data, patents files and more general information services such as PRESTEL. Thus, to gain the maximum benefit from an information handling system, the network must provide gateway facilities to networks in the outside world.

The alternative, without a local area network, would be to employ possibly several terminals to access the different services, each of which would require different procedures and communications facilities. External services would need to be accessed separately by the individuals rather than automatically by the gateway device.

A local area network is not essential to the installation and running of an information management system. However, its existence does make it much easier, and the user can have access to a wider range of services than would be economically possible any other way.

Facsimile

As mentioned in an earlier section, facsimile is the transfer of paper images between two or more locations. Facsimile is generally employed for images which are not easily codable for transmission any other way. For example, text is easily codable with each character being given a unique code. The code is transmitted which can be interpreted by the recipient and the original text reconstructed. If, on the other hand, the sender and recipient wished to transmit a handwritten text exactly as written – possibly for signature verification – then the picture of the text must be transmitted and not the code corresponding to the text. Facsimile is usually employed for photographs, drawings, annotated text, etc. The use of facsimile in a local environment is fairly limited at the present time: the cost of the facsimile terminals and their speed do not justify their use when normal internal mail will suffice. The future Teletex service available from public telecommunications authorities will probably provide a mixed mode (coded text and digitised image).

However, facsimile devices are frequently needed for transmitting information over long distances and so they will be installed in offices. Thus, it is sensible to place them on the local area network, where one exists, so that they are fully integrated members of the electronic office. To be most valuable, the local area network should include a gateway to external networks.

Voice

Without doubt, voice is still the most important medium for communication even within the electronic office. The telephone is still an essential device and is the one 'terminal' which is accessible to the majority of office workers.

The current trend is to digitise the voice signals for transmission and to employ digital switching devices (eg telephone exchanges). Both these techniques offer a number of advantages. Digitised voice can be transmitted without severe degradation and distortion. Digitally controlled private telephone exchanges can operate much faster than their analogue counterparts and can link the caller with the destination very quickly. Digital exchanges can also be programmed easily to provide alternative numbers, voice conferencing, etc, and a user can move offices whilst still retaining the same telephone number without any wiring alterations being needed.

Another very important aspect about digitising voice and telephone exchanges is that voice and data can then be mixed or integrated on the transmission medium. To handle good quality voice traffic requires a transmission capacity of 64 kbps in each direction. This is easily within the capacity of normal local area networks. However, the protocol and service requirements of voice and data are very different.

If we think of a normal telephone conversation, any significant gap in the conversation is disturbing to the listener. He finds it difficult to follow the speech and may think, momentarily, that the link has been broken. Even worse would be the case where individual words were punctuated with gaps. In transmitting data, gaps in the transmission are not usually important, provided they are not too long. The computer or terminal will usually wait for a reasonable length of time before deciding that the link has been lost. Even a line being printed in segments is not very disturbing to the user of a terminal. With data, however, it is essential that all the information received and passed on to the human user or the computer program is correct, with not a bit out of place. Data communications protocols must be able to cater for errors introduced in the transmission. The human ear is much less demanding on accuracy. If a word is distorted or even lost in transmission, the listener can often reconstruct the meaning by examining the rest of the phrase. If a portion cannot be interpreted, the listener has only to ask for it to be repeated.

Thus, speech traffic must be promptly delivered, even if it has errors, and there should be very few delays in transmission so that unacceptable gaps are not introduced between the speaker finishing a phrase and the listener hearing it.

Local area networks are suitable for voice transmission since they have the necessary bandwidth to handle speech without distortion. Some networking techniques are more suitable than others for ensuring that the speech is transmitted quickly and without noticeable gaps. In particular, network access techniques, which ensure that every node is given the opportunity at regular intervals to send information, are generally better for speech than those which rely on contentions with other nodes to give a reasonable average level of use, especially when the latter are carrying a lot of traffic.

Local area networks which provide voice-handling facilities should also provide the ancillary services needed to ensure that the network is used most efficiently. We need, for instance, the equivalent of a dialling and route-making device. On a local network, unless it is star-shaped, all the nodes share the same physical communications channel and every message or packet can be heard by every other. Packets of speech can be sent and addressed individually so that the recipient can distinguish his calls from the others, but certain problems arise if the same node is 'dialled' by two others at the same time. The recipient must be able to accept one call and reject the other. An alternative solution is for a special node on the network to act as a controlling device so that when each call is being set up, this special node can say whether the called number is engaged, not answering or ringing. If another caller then tries to access the same node, the controller will be able to say that it is engaged.

The private telephone exchange (PABX) is the most obvious candidate for adapting to handle voice and data traffic as a local area network. Such networks are sometimes called integrated service networks. The same physical lines joining the telephone to the PABX can also be used for data simultaneously, with the PABX differentiating between the two channels and routeing them accordingly. This has the obvious appeal that no new wiring is needed, since telephone lines of adequate quality are already available to most offices. However, on further examination, it can be seen that as far as handling data is concerned, the idea has some disadvantages. For example, the telephone lines are usually unable to handle high data transmission speeds, which makes them generally unsuitable for bulk data transfer or for use with devices which incorporate processors. Also computers and some other devices need to be in dialogue with several devices simultaneously and this can be difficult to handle in what is essentially a circuit switching PABX.

As well as the fact that new wiring is not generally needed, the PABX approach can have other advantages. One is that the PABX needed to handle mixed data and voice will also be able to handle the more advanced telephone routeing functions: multiple users involved in calls if required; automatic redirection; truncated numbers; hold on to busy numbers and call them when free; etc. The cost of a new PABX to provide these facilities can often be justified for speech alone, and the advantages are more easily quantifiable than for a new local area network.

In the fully integrated electronic office, voice and data transmissions will both be handled but it is not yet clear whether the PABX or the shared-media local area network will provide the communications medium. It seems most likely that the digital PABX will become another node on a local area network, thereby allowing information to pass from one to another. Incoming calls which cannot be connected for some reason to their destination could then be redirected to a file storage device on the local area network where a message would be stored, much like an answering machine. A note would be placed in that user's electronic in-tray to the effect that a telephone message is waiting. (Voice messages can be used as alternatives to text messages.) The user could then dial the device where it is stored using a normal telephone to listen to the message. This, and other new facilities, will become available when voice and data are properly integrated.

Video

The transmission of visual information, other than facsimile, has not become widespread. If moving colour pictures of the quality of television are required, bandwidths of around 6 MHz are necessary for transmission, and circuits with this bandwidth are expensive to obtain, especially when the distances involved are large. Experiments have been made which combine real-time black and white pictures and voice communications devices and have shown that the real value of being able to see the person at the other end of the link has not always been worth the cost of data transmission; often a normal telephone is sufficient.

What has resulted from the limited experiments, however, is that users who are in voice communication often would like to supplement the information they are conveying by means of simple graphics. For example, transmission of a line drawing would be perfectly adequate, either as facsimile or by means of graphics terminals. Transmission of facsimile has already been discussed. It usually takes quite a long time to transmit a complete page as it scans and digitises each line in turn. In the cases where the pictorial information to be transmitted is composed of line drawings, graphs or diagrams, the information can be coded much more easily and transmitted quickly to the other end using normal digital data transmission speeds, where it is reassembled by the receiving terminal into a copy of the original. Both these facilities are possible now using transmission lines of normal bandwidth. Once a picture is sent, it does not need to be sent again until a change is made, unlike real-time television pictures.

By developing the idea of transmitting simple images, an electronic 'sketch-pad' or 'blackboard' can be envisaged in which both the sender and receiver can alter the image and then transmit it to the other. By these means, two workers can discuss and amend a drawing, or any other pictorial information, using a telephone suitably enhanced by the addition of a low-speed graphics terminal.

The applications just discussed are of most value where the two people involved are too far apart for a face-to-face meeting to be feasible. It is doubtful if there is very much need for video transmission within a single site, unless it is very large. Because video and graphics terminals are much more expensive to provide than are simple workstations, most organisations will, in the near future, be unwilling to provide a bulk set of such facilities for all their users. This limited cover of the potential population will also limit the amount of use which is made. Ironically, the latest developments in local area networks are ideally suited to the transmission of video information. Local area networks almost always have a high data transmission rate and can therefore support the rather larger capacity required for visual information better than the traditional low-speed links.

Those local area networking techniques which require all the users to share one data communications channel are not suitable for real-time video transmission for two reasons. First, the bandwidth available is only just sufficient for real-time colour pictures with sound, but this leaves little extra for the other users. Second, real-time traffic demands that capacity is available the whole time and transmission cannot be interrupted for more than a fraction of a second at a time. Even a single conversation of this type is sufficient to load the network almost to its full extent and special priority must be assigned to it to prevent other conversations from fragmenting the information flow. If the visual information transmitted is of the graphical or blackboard type, or if slow-scan television is used, the load will be considerably less and a fragmented dialogue will have no noticeable effect on the quality.

Broadband local area networks are based on technology which originated in the cable television market and hence represent a perfect solution to transmitting real-time colour pictures. The techniques used by broadband transmission will not be discussed fully in this chapter, but suffice to say that a considerable number of video channels can be shared within a single coaxial cable. Data channels can also use the cable but need much less bandwidth. In this way, a number of simultaneous video conversations can take place on a broadband local area network without interfering with, or being interfered with by, the data transmissions also taking place.

Many observers claim that the broadband technique for local area networks is the one which will become the norm because of its advantages and enormous bandwidth – 300 MHz – compared with around 20 MHz for other techniques.

Thus, we can see that the technology supports video transmissions. It remains to be seen whether there will be the demand within a single organisation on a single site, and whether the equipment needed to meet the demands will be developed.

Data Processing Services

Within an office, access to data processing resources is essential for most organisations. The requirements are very varied and can range from the ability to run computer programs from a remote location, or enter them into a job queue for later running, to accessing a centrally maintained database to read the information contained in it. As the processing capabilities of the terminals and workstations scattered around the site increase, the number of data processing services needed by a network will also increase.

The oldest requirement is remote job entry. This facility permits a user to enter a job for processing on a computer system in another place. The printed output either appears at the device at which the job has been entered, or a message is sent to it to the effect that the job has run and the output can be obtained from computer reception. In networks where several computers are linked, different jobs may be run on different computers without the user necessarily knowing which.

In addition to the above, the following services may also be required:

—   remote access to central computing facilities;

—   personal computer: each manager and professional, with a work-station in a network, may want to use it as a 'super' pocket calculator;

—   file transfer and file sharing: moving files from one computer to another, and the use of a shared filestore;

—   terminal access to other users and computers;

—   access to external services provided by other networks and organisations.

Most current local area network technologies are able to support the above requirements in terms of the transmission speeds and carrying capacity which they offer. The services which they provide are usually of a lower level than those required. These have to be added on to the network once installed.

The only service which may prove a strain on the local area network is the transference of large quantities of information from one computer system to another, since the speed with which a computer can output data is of the same order as the network transmission speed itself.

The requirement to link to externally supplied services means that a gateway or bridging device is needed between the local network and an external system. This is required whether we are considering a local area network or an on-site computing system. Most suppliers of computer-based networks provide facilities to link to external systems, either in the form of a public telephone network interface, a device for a public packet switched system, or the ability to use leased circuits. Most local area network products, when they appear on the market, will have these facilities.

CONCLUSIONS

Local area networks can be used in many areas of data processing and the electronic office. Indeed it is not an exaggeration to say that some applications will not be developed to their greatest extent without them. The integrated electronic office is just not possible without some form of local area network.

The question which should be asked is how many services should the local area network provide:

— should it be a highly reliable, available, and fast transmission service only?

— should it be capable of handling different makes and types of equipment?

— should it provide some central shared storage facilities?

— should it provide electronic messaging, word processing, personal information handling services, archiving, etc?

— should access be provided to corporate information services?

— should it provide printing and copying facilities?

— should there be access to external services (Prestel, Telex, Teletex, etc)?

— should voice and data be integrated?

— should data processing and personal computing facilities be provided?

— how many video services should be available?

— is a telephone answering and voice message storage facility required?

The answers to these questions are dependent on the requirements of the individual organisations and the availability of suitable products. As with everything else, the more facilities which a local area network has, the more it will cost to buy, run and maintain. The trade-off is between the cheap and simple local communications facility upon which the purchaser has to build the required services, and the costly developed network which will be inherently more difficult to adapt at a time when the requirements are still a bit hazy.

Common to many requirements is the need for a gateway device to link the local area network to the outside world. Its precise functions depend on the exact requirements and the outside networks which are to be used. For example:

(1) *Local area network to public switched system.* The public network can be used to access remote computers, terminals, networks, services and other organisations. These can also access the local area network if they have permission.

(2) *Local area network to mainframe computer network.* This would allow devices on the local area network to use facilities in the computer network. The requirement is for a gateway to emulate the terminal protocols acceptable to the mainframe.

3 Technologies Available

INTRODUCTION

In Chapter 1, the particular characteristics which distinguish a local area network from any other type of network were discussed. It was concluded that if wide area or long-haul networks interconnect devices on separate sites, and system buses interconnect separate processors within a single piece of equipment or a room, then local area networks cover the area in between. They interconnect separate devices on a single site.

The restricted area covered by a local area network is the basic feature which can be assumed for all of them. Practically every other characteristic can be derived as a consequence of this feature, and of the cheapness and compactness now possible for the electronic components which are needed to support the network.

In this chapter, the main requirements of a local area network are identified. The way in which these can be satisfied, and the consequences for design, are also discussed.

MAIN REQUIREMENTS

Once the decision has been made to keep the network within the confines of a single office building, factory or site, the designer and user are free to choose whatever technology suits their needs best. The user interface to the network does not have to be the same as those dictated by the public telecommunications authorities, and so a simple interface which is tailored to the particular needs of the user can be devised. In practice, of course, things are not quite so straightforward, as we shall see when the other requirements are considered. In theory, an unrestricted information transmission system which can work at a sufficiently high speed to satisfy every user, and which has enough capacity to cope with all the traffic offered to it, has great appeal, but these things can only be obtained at some cost.

Let us first of all list the main requirements. (The remainder of the chapter discusses how the requirements can be met using the available technology. The next chapter shows how the resulting network can be shared by many devices.)

Low Cost

By *low cost* is meant that the cost of the mechanism for connecting together the devices is low compared with the cost of the devices themselves. Thus the solution for connecting together expensive mainframe computers could be very different from the solutions for microcomputers or terminals. Naturally the other requirements for data transmission between mainframes are also significantly different, so that characteristic alone could result in a totally different network.

High Transmission Speed

The aim of a high transmission speed is to enable information to be moved from one location to another with the minimum of delay, so that devices can respond as quickly, or so it seems to the user, as they would if they were connected directly to the processors. To computer designers and users, the rate at which information is transmitted by the normal telecommunications network is very slow when compared with the data bus and peripheral access speeds with which they are familiar. Local area networks offer the potential to exchange data between separate devices at a rate comparable with normal computer working speeds.

Network Capacity

Network capacity is a measure of the ability of the network to handle the information which is presented to it by all the attached devices. It is closely related to transmission speed, since unless each conversation on the network is given a channel which is completely separate from every other one, the available capacity will have to be shared by a number of users. The longer a message takes to pass through the network, the longer will others have to wait. There are ways round the problem for circuits with slow transmission speeds (such as frequency division multiplexing), which are discussed later.

Low Error Rate

Traditional data transmission techniques have exhibited relatively high error rates when transmitting data. Various ways of reducing the transmission errors, and of detecting them reliably when they do occur, have been devised, but generally errors are still more frequent than those experienced in computers. To the designer of a computer-based piece of equipment, a network that gives as few errors as does the computer technology would allow simplified hardware and software to be incorporated. Local area networks, with their short distances, offer the potential for fewer transmission errors.

Reliability

The data transmission network must be very reliable; failure makes it impossible for the users to perform their normal distributed computing functions and resource sharing, thereby losing most of the benefits of placing computers in different locations. In most cases the physical medium for interconnecting devices (usually a cable) is inherently reliable but the devices connected to it to make the medium carry the information in the required form are far less so. The designer of a local area network chooses the method of coding the information for sending through the medium in such a way that the devices to drive it and the method of access can be simplified. Thus the overall reliability is improved.

Easy to Connect to

A major problem in interconnecting computers today is the variety of different connection procedures and transmission protocols. It is virtually impossible to connect together computing devices from more than one manufacturer and be confident that they will be able to exchange meaningful information. A local area network should help to provide some degree of compatibility between attached devices and should itself not present any new problems when devices are connected to it.

Mixed Traffic

The convergence of computing and communications and their use in office procedures has been a discussion topic for some time and we are now seeing the first examples in the electronic office. Convergence brings with it the problem of handling information in many different forms:

digital data, text, voice, video, facsimile and signalling. The optimum requirements for each of these differ so radically that hitherto few transmission systems have attempted to cater for more than one at a time. No current public telecommunications systems satisfactorily serve more than one class of use, but a purely private network could be designed using the latest technology to cover a wide range of information types.

Use with Other Networks

It would be irresponsible for any designer of computer systems not to recognise that his equipment may be used with equipment from another source. Similarly, computer networks are likely to be interconnected, either through a private or public network. Although local area networks are wholly contained within one site, they will not be totally isolated from users, terminals, computers and networks in other locations. Local area networks at two or more sites are likely to be linked in order that the devices on one can send information to devices on another. These networks will have to be linked by means of private or public wide area networks. Thus, local area networks must provide facilities to use other networks where these are appropriate.

Services

As well as providing the basic service of moving information cheaply and quickly from one location to another, a local area network will also provide access to services provided by systems using the network. It should also provide what are best described as network services designed to enhance the network for the users. The services that are provided as part of the network are the choice of the designer of the network but they would typically include fault monitoring, printing and a central filestore. These are extras to the basic local area network but are considered by many potential users as being essential to make the network a useful addition to the existing computing and communications facilities.

CLASSIFICATION OF TECHNOLOGIES

Local area networks can be classified in a number of ways, none of which are wholly convenient for all circumstances:

1) *Physical transmission medium used*
   What kind of interconnection medium is used in the network? Possibilities include: coaxial cable, twisted-pair cable, flat ribbon cable, fibre optics, radio and infra-red transmission.

2) *Network topology*

How are the devices in the network physically connected together? Typical configurations are: star, ring, loop, bus, tree, mesh, fully interconnected, and combinations of these.

3) *Transmission mode*

Transmission mode refers to the way information is moved from one location to another and how it is structured to do this. Most existing systems are based on packet switching principles but others such as circuit switching, point-to-point and broadcast are all used, either on their own or in combination with others.

4) *Resource-sharing mechanism or mode of operation*

The techniques used for gaining access to the network and the way the available capacity is used are other possible ways of looking at local area networks. The different multiplexing techniques, the contention algorithms and the rules to be followed in order to use the network, are all considered under this heading.

There is a good deal of overlap between classes. For example, packet switching is both a transmission mode for the network and a network resource-sharing mechanism.

Some modes of operation are also applicable only to particular topologies or physical transmission media. For example, ring topologies require specialised access techniques and modes of operation. Each way of classifying local area networks tends to be suitable for some ways of looking at the problem and equally unsuitable for others.

TRANSMISSION MEDIA

In its simplest form, a local area network consists of a physical medium (typically an electrical cable) linking a set of user stations which themselves contain sufficient logic and electronic circuits to enable them to use the network. Figure 3.1 shows the typical configuration at a tap in the network.

In this section the physical transmission media are examined. In many local area networks the medium can be one of several options, or even combinations of media, but most experimental systems and current products are designed around one particular medium. There are essentially two schools of thought regarding the choice of the medium. One says let us choose the cheapest possible, consistent with the speed and reliability requirements. The other says that since the medium is going to be shared

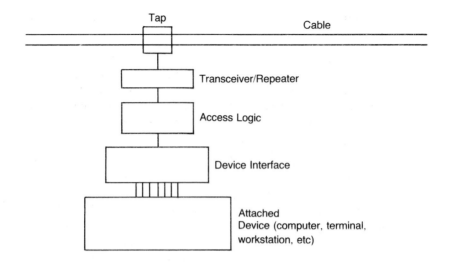

Figure 3.1   Tapping into a Local Area Network

by a large number of users, and the prime requirement is high speed and low error rate, then the best interconnection medium should be used regardless of cost. Other requirements and practical considerations naturally influence the final choice regardless of cost criteria used.

In examining the characteristics of the transmission media and their suitability for local area networks, the following features must be taken into consideration:

— *Bandwidth*
  Bandwidth is the width of the frequency band that can be handled efficiently by the system. Indirectly it is also a measure of the transmission speed which can be supported by that system; a high transmission speed demands a system with a high bandwidth. It is not just a function of the physical medium, but also of the whole system needed to send and receive the information. Once digital information is on the physical medium, the rate at which it can move from one location to another is a function only of the medium itself; for electrical signals on a wire this will be approximately three quarters of the speed of light. It is only the rate at which the state of the signals on the medium can be changed which determines the rate at which information can be transmitted. The

state of the medium can only be changed by the devices which are attached to it to drive it.

— *Connectivity*
Some physical transmission media are suitable for broadcast information, whilst others are better suited for point-to-point links. Some media also need extra devices such as repeaters to preserve the signals over relatively long distances.

— *Geographic coverage possible*
The maximum distance between stations on a link, and the total area which a local area network can cover, without loss of signal strength or unacceptable degradation of quality of service, do not just depend on the characteristics of the physical media alone. If the delay between one station sending a message and the destination receiving it is too long, the algorithm which is used to gain access to the network can be affected. If it takes too long for a message to reach all the devices on the network in a broadcast system, for example, then two or more users may well try to transmit at the same time. The overall result could be a reduction in throughput on the network due to interference between devices.

— *Site topology*
Some physical media used for local area networks are better suited to particular site topologies than others. The location of the devices to be connected to the network will dictate the path the interconnection medium must follow and this may be difficult to accommodate with certain media. Allied to this are the requirements imposed by the various building and safety regulations, some of which may impose severe constraints on the choice of the medium and the route it can take.

— *Noise immunity*
Ideally the physical medium chosen to transmit information should be free from interference from every outside source, but in practice this is not possible. Some media are relatively free from interference, whilst with others it is notoriously difficult to prevent extraneous signals and noise from corrupting the information being transmitted. As well as interference from outside signals, there is also the problem of noise generated by other devices such as electric motors. Noise is random information of varying amp-

litudes which is added to the signals being transmitted. Interference is other information from another source. Distortion can also be considered under this heading. This is where the signal is changed by the medium itself during transit.

— *Security*
Some kinds of physical transmission media radiate the signal they are carrying to their surroundings so that any unscrupulous person can place a pick-up device close to the medium in order to eavesdrop on the messages which are being transmitted. Some media radiate much more than others, making the task of a potential eavesdropper easier. In some cases it may be possible for an eavesdropper to actually tap the medium directly rather than rely on the radiation. This can be very difficult to detect with some media without actually examining every part of the network, which can be almost impossible if the medium is ducted. In other cases the presence of an illegal tap can be readily detected due to changes in the transmission characteristics of the network.

— *Transmission technologies*
Allied with the choice of medium and the topology of the network is the method by which information is moved from the source to the destination. The first choice is between whether a digital or an analogue technique for the signal is used. Then various methods of modulating the signal to provide the information carrying capability can be employed, from an unmodulated system (baseband) to many different analogue modulation techniques, each with their own advantages and disadvantages. As well as consideration of the modulation techniques, the way the information is structured for transmission can be affected by the properties of the physical media. Although packetising the information has become the accepted method for data transmission, the format of the packets, the addressing and the amount of error-checking information needed in the packet are affected by the quality of the service possible from the underlying physical medium.

— *Cost*
Cost can be subdivided into the cost of the physical medium, its installation, maintenance and the cost of the equipment needed to make it provide the kind of service which the user wants. As must be expected with a relatively new technology, especially one which

involves a quantity of electronic circuitry, the cost is likely to reduce rapidly when the quantity required is sufficient to warrant the change from discrete components to integrated circuits which can be manufactured cheaply in quantity.

— *Availability*
Not least among the considerations of the physical transmission medium for local area networks is its availability or otherwise. The very fact that certain types of cable were to hand during the initial design stage of some local area networks has contributed to a major extent to their use for that system. In many cases other media would have produced superior results but were not so easily obtainable at the time. Generally the easier the medium is to obtain, the cheaper it will be to buy.

— *Restrictions imposed*
The choice of a particular physical transmission medium is likely to restrict the things which can be done with the network and the transmission technologies which can be used. For example, if optic fibres are used, it is considerably more difficult to design a broadcast network which can be tapped without disturbing the other users and the characteristics of the network as a whole. Optic fibres themselves may offer sufficient advantages to the user that he is willing to live with the restrictions, but this depends on many other factors which have to be taken into consideration when the whole network is being designed.

The main types of transmission media in use will be examined in the context of the above requirements.

Twisted-Pair Cable

Standard telephone or telex terminal cable in which one or more pairs of wires are contained within a single outer case is in very common use in office buildings. Each pair of wires is twisted together in a helix in an attempt to provide fairly constant electrical characteristics. The general form of a twisted-pair cable is shown in Figure 3.2.

Twisted-pair cable is suited to both analogue and digital transmission even though its major area of use is for transmission of analogue speech. For a number of reasons, it is best suited for transmission of information over relatively short distances. The attenuation of a signal during transit

Figure 3.2   Twisted-Pair Cable

can be fairly high and its waveform can be distorted. To minimise these problems, repeaters are commonly employed in the line to amplify the signal and regenerate the waveform.

The bandwidth of a network based on twisted-pair cables depends on: quality of the conductors used, accuracy of the length of each component of the pair and the techniques used to drive the information along the cable. With careful choice and installation of cable, information transmission rates of several million bits per second over short distances (a few hundred metres) can be reliably achieved. By means of repeaters placed at shorter intervals in the cable and by using specialised electronics and transmission techniques, transfer rates as high as 100 Mbps can be reached.

By its very nature, twisted-pair cable is best suited for point-to-point links between devices or repeaters on the network. It is not often used as a broadcast medium because a broadcast bus usually needs to be fairly long, distortion-free and passive. Tapping into a twisted-pair cable is not easy without disturbing the other users on the medium or without changing the transmission characteristics significantly.

Twisted-pair cable of the kind normally and readily available is not shielded, and consequently it radiates to its surroundings when it is carrying information. This makes it very easy for an eavesdropper to place a pick-up coil alongside the cable to listen to the transmission without any fear of detection by devices on the cable, since the transmission characteristics remain effectively unchanged. Shielding can be provided at extra cost to reduce but not eliminate the radiation, and the individual wires in the cable can be balanced to help with this, but the main improvements obtained by these techniques are evident at frequencies below about 100 kHz. To be of most use, local area networks should operate at much higher frequencies and hence higher data transmission rates.

Twisted-pair cable typically has a high electrical capacitance which can severely distort the signal which it carries. The high capacitance can be partially offset by means of loading coils, but again the benefits of these are experienced mainly at lower frequencies than are considered useful for local area networks.

Hence it may seem strange that something as unsuitable for high-speed data transmission as twisted-pair telephone cable should have been used as widely as it has. The reasons for its adoption are its availability, its very low cost and the fact that it is a well-understood transmission medium which lends itself to a variety of different modes of use – a very valuable feature for an experimental system. However, against this must be offset the large amount of care which is needed to adequately install it in order to achieve the desired transmission speeds. Also the fact that repeaters and other extra electronic devices are needed to ensure the cable performs in the right sort of manner for high-speed digital data transmission over a sufficiently wide area adds significantly to the installation cost, thereby removing most of its cost advantages over some of its rivals.

Multi-Way Cable

Round multi-core or flat ribbon cable can be used successfully for local area networks. Many of the characteristics of twisted-pair cable (eg high attenuation, susceptibility to electrical interference and ease of installation) are shared by multi-way cable.

Its main virtue is the fact that the control and data signals can be transmitted separately using different conductors, thus simplifying the interface problems. One conductor can be allocated as the 'busy' indicator. When a device is actually transmitting on the network, this conductor can be switched on to indicate to the other users that the network is busy. One or more other conductors can be assigned to sending synchronisation signals. By doing this, there is no need for special encoding methods which incorporate clocking signals. Also, several conductors can be allocated to transmitting the data, so parallel rather than serial bit streams can be put onto the cable, the actual number of bits being determined by the number of conductors available.

The overall result of using the conductors in this manner is that the interface devices necessary to put information onto the medium, detect when someone else is transmitting, and read information off, can be simplified. High data transmission rates are possible if sufficient parallel conductors are used.

Against this must be weighed the fact that multi-way cable is much more expensive than either twisted-pair or ordinary coaxial cable. However, it is equally suitable for ring topologies and for bus systems which operate in a baseband mode. Data transmission rates in excess of 10 Mbps are achievable.

Coaxial Cable

Coaxial cable consists of a single central conductor surrounded by a concentric layer of dielectric material which is surrounded by a metal screen which can be either solid or a mesh of wire. The whole assembly is protected from the outside environment by another layer which is usually an insulating material. Figure 3.3 shows the components of typical coaxial cables.

Coaxial cable is available in a wide variety of qualities ranging from the cheap and relatively low-quality cable aimed at the domestic radio, television and hi-fi markets to that of very high quality which has low-loss transmission characteristics, high immunity from interference and resilience to accidental damage. The latter can be very expensive and, because

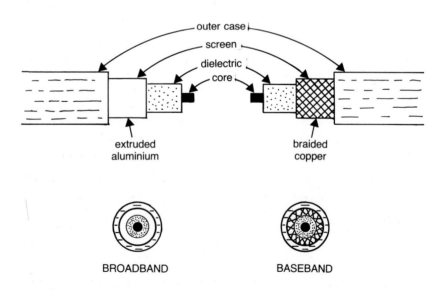

Figure 3.3   Coaxial Cable Types

it can be very stiff, it can be difficult to install, even to the extent of requiring special equipment to bend it round corners.

The electrical characteristics of coaxial cable make it eminently suitable for transmitting high-frequency signals whilst at the same time reducing the radiation from the cable and remaining almost immune from interference. Very little cross-talk is experienced between coaxial cables running alongside each other. Because of its inherently good features, very high data transmission rates using both digital and analogue techniques are possible.

In the case of local area networks, the usual coaxial cable used is of middle-of-the-road quality used by suppliers of cable television, commonly called CATV, which stands for Community Antenna TeleVision. Cable television is used by about a quarter of the homes in the USA: hence the cable is widely available and the techniques for installing it are well understood. Added to this, equipment for tapping the cable, and amplifying the signal if analogue transmission is being used, is readily available 'off the shelf'. The requirements of the domestic cable television industry dictate that the equipment used has a very high reliability since much of it will be outside and in relatively inaccessible positions. The mean time between failures of the line amplifiers is several years.

Two modes of data transmission are possible using coaxial cable: baseband and broadband. In baseband signalling, the information is put onto the cable in essentially an unmodulated form. Each bit of data is represented by a discrete level of signal on the cable. Broadband, on the other hand, uses modulation techniques to transmit analogue signals. The differences between baseband and broadband transmission are discussed in much more detail in a later section, together with the different techniques which are used to access and control the use of the medium.

The types of coaxial cable used for baseband and broadband differ slightly in their design. That now used for baseband generally has a wire mesh screen made of copper and has a characteristic impedance of 50 ohms. The cable used for broadband is usually of heavier construction, having a screen made of extruded aluminium and with a characteristic impedance of 75 ohms.

The bandwidth of coaxial cable depends on the mode of transmission being employed; ie whether baseband or modulated signalling is being used. With baseband, the capabilities of the electronics which drive the medium largely determine the speed of transmission, but 10 Mbps is fairly easy to achieve; much higher rates are possible at increased cost. The bandwidth of broadband systems is typically around 300 MHz, giving a possible digital data transmission rate of around 150 Mbps full-duplex. In practice, however, the available frequency bandwidth of a broadband system is divided into a number of discrete channels, the width of each being determined by the way they are used.

Baseband systems use an essentially passive physical medium and consequently they can be tapped without significantly disturbing the medium's characteristics. This is an advantage when new devices are being added but it is a positive security risk. Incidently, the fact that baseband signalling does not use modulation means that the cable radiates more than it would do if it were modulated. Thus it is easier to eavesdrop on a baseband network than on a broadband system.

Coaxial cable is ideally suited to a broadcast network system with each user attaching to the network wherever required. The geographic coverage possible depends on a large number of factors. In principle, coaxial cable can cover long distances, provided that amplifiers and repeaters are inserted into the lines at appropriate intervals, but certain transmission techniques and access methods require that the transmission delay, distortion and attenuation be restricted to an acceptable level, which itself severely restricts the acceptable cable length. When we come to examine the methods employed for sharing a network, we will see that maximum end-to-end transmission delay greatly influences the length of cable used and the size of the packets of data which can be transmitted. Each must be traded off against the others.

Using typical CATV coaxial cable, the actual cost is a little higher than twisted-pair, but the cost of connecting to it and the lower cost of shielding it for security reasons may make the two comparable. Against this should be weighed the extra installation costs caused by the limited flexibility of coaxial cable of adequate quality.

Fibre Optics

Fibre optic cable differs from the types of cable previously discussed in that it transmits light rather than electrical signals. The cable consists of a filament for transmitting the light which is usually made from silica but can be plastic for low-quality installations. The light-conducting material is surrounded by another substance with a lower refractive index which minimises the loss through the cable and guides the rays of light by means of internal reflections.

The principle of transmission of light through a tube of glass containing water was demonstrated as long ago as 1870, but it was not until the 1950s that glass rods were coated with a suitable refractive material that the idea became a commercial product. The first optic fibres were used for transmitting images and were often used by surgeons for examining internal parts of the body without surgery. It was not until lasers and light-emitting diodes were applied to the task of transmitting light along optic fibres that they were used for digital data transmission. This, and the discovery of low-loss fibres, led in the 1970s to the development of optic fibres as a possible alternative to copper cables for the transmission of information. The basic raw material of optic fibres is silica which is potentially cheaper than copper and, provided it is of high enough quality, should be able to offer a much higher bandwidth, and hence a higher transmission rate.

Various types and quality of optic fibre are available which, coupled with different types of light source, permit a wide range of transmission rates at a wide range of costs. Figure 3.4 shows some single fibre types:

— Multimode step index
   This is a fairly dispersive type of fibre and is generally used in applications where it is important that the fibres can be joined together easily.

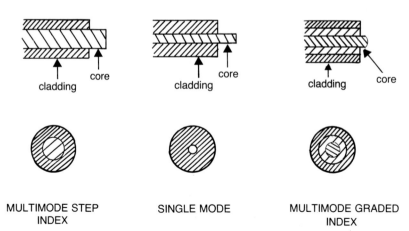

Figure 3.4   Optic Fibres

—   Multimode graded index
    This fibre has a refractive index that varies with the radius. It is
    fairly easy to join together.

—   Single mode
    Single mode fibre has a central filament which is very fine. As a
    consequence, it is difficult to join two ends together. The fibre
    does have advantages for data transmission over other types
    because it can support much higher transmission rates.

It will be seen from the figure that optic fibre filaments are very small
compared with traditional copper wires. Thus, more optic filaments than
copper cables can be put in ducts.

Using the best quality fibres, a very small amount of light is lost in the
cable. Experimental lengths of fibre with a loss of only 0.5 dB/km have
been made, but using fibres of a much lower quality, transmission rates of
around 50 Mbps over several kilometres can be obtained.

One great advantage of optic fibres over traditional electrical conductors is their immunity to electrical interference which makes them especially suitable for electrically hostile environments. Also the information
which they carry cannot be detected merely by placing a pick-up alongside, so making them more secure from unauthorised eavesdroppers.

A single optic fibre is essentially a one-way transmission medium, with
a light source at one end and a detector at the other (Figure 3.5).
Two-way transmission is possible by means of a pair of cables, one
carrying information in one direction and the other in the other direction.

Tapping into a fibre is not easy to do since generally the light path must
be interrupted and the information regenerated and retransmitted again
in the original direction. There are techniques for reading the information
from a fibre optic cable without breaking it but these require special
cables and even then they are not wholly satisfactory. Optical fibres are
ideally suited to ring and loop topologies, but the difficulty in tapping
makes them less suitable for broadcast bus systems.

Each electrical connection to an optical fibre requires a special device
to convert electrical signals to corresponding light pulses. The reverse
system is required at each point where the cable is tapped. When repeaters are required, these must be optical-to-optical amplifiers. Since these
devices are not yet as readily available as electrical amplifiers and inter-

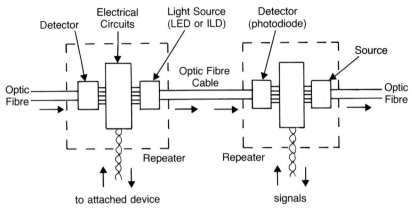

Figure 3.5 Data Transmission with Optic Fibres

face units, the cost of using an optic fibre link can be quite large. Since optical fibres are not yet mass-produced in the same way that copper cables are, the actual cost of optic fibres at the present time is greater than the cost of copper cables. However, in situations where very high transmission rates, good noise immunity, light weight (eg in aircraft) or security are required, optic fibres can provide the best solution.

Radio Transmission

If the intention was to find the transmission medium which is widely available to everybody, then radio transmission would be the obvious choice. The transmission medium is the 'luminiferous ether' which was thought of as the medium needed to carry all electromagnetic radiation through space. This is the origin of the name 'Ethernet' (although Ethernet chose to use coaxial cables!). One of the earliest systems which could be thought of as a local area network, even though it covered a greater area than that commonly accepted for a local area network now, was the ALOHA network in Hawaii. This network used radio transmission as the means of connecting a number of outlying stations with a central computing system. The ALOHA network demonstrates many of the techniques now used by other broadcast networks and its main features are discussed elsewhere in this book.

There are a number of problems associated with radio transmission which make it unsuitable for most local area network applications. One is that radio transmission is not restricted to the confines of the one office block or industrial site and so it is easy for transmission to be interfered with by other people outside using the same frequency channels. It is also easy for an eavesdropper to listen undetected to any transmissions made using the radio waves, so any security must be provided by an extra level within the systems which are using the ether for information transmission.

The communications bandwidth available to a user of a radio channel is a function of the frequency band and modulation technique which is being used. In order that the available frequency bands can be made available to as many different groups of users as possible, the individual channels are restricted in width so the actual transmission rates are also severely restricted in practice.

The range of the transmission possible is also a function of the frequency band used. Generally the higher the frequency band used, the wider the bandwidth which is possible, but the shorter the range. Greater range can be achieved using more powerful equipment but then the greater is the likelihood of interfering with other users.

Radio communications are very susceptible to noise and electrical interference, so a mechanism for detecting and correcting errors which are caused by extraneous factors needs to be included in any design.

Radio's most promising area of application is in linking high-speed local area networks which themselves use another technology. Currently under investigation are systems which use satellites (for example, Project Universe, mentioned in Chapter 1).

Other Techniques

Of other possible transmission media, only infra-red and light beams have received any real consideration. Both have the problem that they can be obstructed by any solid object or even certain weather conditions, and this severely restricts their use.

Infra-red transmission has been thought of in the context of a single room, possibly an open plan office. An infra-red transmitter/receiver would be placed on the ceiling and all the devices in that part of the network would be within sight of it. The technique is familiar with domestic remote controlled televisions. In the office environment, the transmitter/receiver would be connected by ordinary cable to the rest of the network. Apart from the obstruction problem already mentioned, the transmitter/receiver is the weak point in the network since all the communications in that area must go through it.

Infra-red has the advantage that it is unobtrusive, easy to install and has sufficient bandwidth for its range of application. It is very easy to eavesdrop on other conversations and to interfere with transmissions in the same area and within sight of the transmitter/receiver. Within the range of application, these factors do not pose a serious threat. For quick installation of devices in offices where they may be moved around frequently, infra-red is a serious contender.

Infra-red and visible light can also be used to provide communications between buildings. For this class of application, relatively high data transmission rates are usually required, so lasers are employed for the transmitters. Laser technology for data transmission is also used in fibre optics, so the technique is familiar. It is especially suitable for providing cheap, high-bandwidth links between buildings, provided these are within sight of each other. Using the technique, several million bits per second can be transmitted reliably.

TOPOLOGIES

The topology of a network is the pattern of the nodes and their interconnection. Topology has in the past been used as a means of categorising local networks. This was useful only when there were a few different local networks and their topology did in fact indicate the way the network operated as well as the interconnection of the nodes. Since local area networks have proliferated, the same topology can be operated in many different ways; a classification based on some other criterion, such as the access mechanism or the network control technique, is more useful. In spite of this, a discussion of network topologies is still useful to aid the later descriptions of the techniques and also since some techniques apply best to particular topologies.

Star

The most common topology for installations which are designed round a central mainframe computer system is the star network (Figure 3.6). The

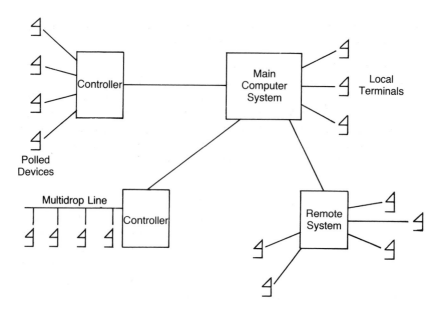

Figure 3.6   Star Mainframe Computer System

centre of the star can perform processing and/or switching of messages from one incoming line to another. More complex networks can be constructed by interconnecting the stars. One feature of this kind of topology is that each outlying device is connected to the central system by means of a line which is for its exclusive use or which is shared by only a small number of others on a polled basis. The shared resource in a star network is the central system and not the transmission medium as in the case of a true local area network.

In principle, the addition of new devices is easy in a star network because each one just needs to be tapped into an existing multidropped line, or a new line is put in between it and the central system. In practice, it is not quite so straightforward. The installation of each new cable necessitates the whole route between the two sites being accessed in order to put the wire into ducts. The communications-handling device at the central site also needs to have a suitable port available and the necessary communications software to handle the particular device which is being put on. Thus in a star computer network which is serving 20 separate terminals, for example, a communications controller with 20 ports is needed with 20 separate lines between it and the terminals.

A star computer network generally operates in a polled mode with each outlying device being asked in turn if it has any information to send. If it has, the communications controller gives its full attention to that device until either there is no more information to be sent or the controller decides to give another device a chance. If the central device acts only as a switch, two devices can be connected together for a time so that they can exchange messages. During this exchange, other pairs of devices can be in conversation without affecting any other dialogues.

The star is an important topology for local area networks. The hub is used primarily as a switch for connecting together the peripheral terminals, workstations, computers, etc. This is the purpose of the normal private on-site telephone network where the peripheral devices are telephones. In this form star networks will become local area networks, with suitably enhanced exchanges at the centre. This important topic will be considered in more detail in a later chapter.

Loop

A loop network (Figure 3.7) consists of a controlling device which has only two cables attached to it, one for outgoing messages and one for incoming messages. All the terminals and other devices on the network are connected to the loop of cable and share it to send messages to other devices on the loop. This configuration has been in existence for some time as an optional way of connecting a small number of terminals to a computer, provided that the quantity of information which they each have to send is relatively small.

The way the actual loop is shared amongst the devices connected to it depends largely on the supplier. One way is to poll each device in turn by means of a specially addressed packet. Devices ready to send can respond in a way determined by the protocol. Another way is for the controlling device to periodically send an empty packet around the loop and any device which has information to send is at liberty to put its data into the packet. With this technique, unless every device sends information infrequently, some mechanism must be devised to prevent one user from hogging the whole network.

Because the transmission medium is shared by every device on the

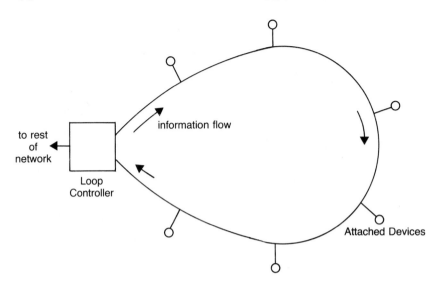

Figure 3.7   Loop Network

network, a loop can be thought of as a local area network. However, past implementations of loops have usually employed only relatively low-speed transmission lines with the result that the devices which can be served effectively are severely limited, both in number and in speed. There is no reason why the transmission lines used could not be capable of carrying data at high speed – in which case many more devices could be served, provided that a suitable method of sharing the capacity could be devised.

A loop should not be confused with a ring, although superficially they are similar in appearance. A loop has a device which controls the use of the network by all the devices which are connected to it, whereas a ring does not. The ring topology is discussed in more detail in the following section.

Ring

A ring network (Figure 3.8) consists of a set of nodes, each one of which is connected to the nodes on each side of it and to no other. None of these nodes is responsible for controlling the network as a whole and each has equal status.

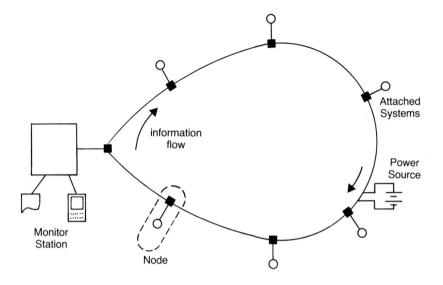

Figure 3.8   Ring Network

Ring networks were developed as computer networks as a result of looking for an efficient means of connecting together all the devices which need to be on the network. The aim was a network which would be both cheap and easy to control so that no one node could gain exclusive use of the network and every user would have a fair share of the available capacity. The challenge of the ring concept is in designing a system which would be both fair and yet with a sufficiently simple method of control that a separate controller is not needed, and each node does not require to be excessively complicated.

Most existing rings are unidirectional in that information is received at one side of each node and is transmitted from the other. Bidirectional rings are possible but are necessarily much more complicated, in terms of the wiring which is required, the control mechanism which must be employed, and the higher level protocols needed to ensure that messages are received in order and erroneous ones are detected and retransmitted.

Ring networks usually operate by means of a special message being passed from one node to the next. On receipt of this message that node is then able to transmit a packet of information. All the other nodes on the network will receive the information packet and will examine the address field to see if that packet is intended for them. If it is, they read it into a buffer and in some schemes they mark the original packet as having been received. Since everyone on the ring can actually receive each packet, it is easy to implement a broadcast message facility.

Many methods for transmitting information around a ring have been devised (discussed in detail in the next chapter). They all operate by giving permission to transmit to a node which then is able to put a limited amount of information on the ring before handing over to another node.

Rings are capable of being run at a very high speed by means of suitable electronics at the points where the ring is tapped for the nodes. The actual observed point-to-point information transfer rate depends to a large extent on the methods used to control and access the ring.

Being usually unidirectional, rings are ideally suited to the use of optical fibres as the transmission medium. Most current ring-based products can either be obtained with fibre optics as an option or can easily be adapted. Some are even available with fibre optics as the standard.

Rings are sometimes criticised with respect to their reliability, since the information is circulated round every node, and each tap must be able both to listen to the transmissions and to regenerate the message and retransmit it to the next node. The hardware which receives and retransmits the message is usually kept separate from the rest of the node so that the node can be switched off without affecting the operation of the ring as a whole. This hardware is usually called the repeater and in some cases is powered separately from the attached device itself. In other cases, relays are used to bypass the repeater if it fails or power to it is cut off. To ensure adequate reliability, the power is often supplied through the network itself by means of redundant systems. This is more difficult to achieve with a fibre optic ring than with one using normal copper cables.

The cable used in a ring network depends on the choice of the supplier and can be coaxial cable, twisted-pair telephone cable or fibre optics. The mode of transmission is usually baseband and the repeaters perform the minimum necessary to accept and transmit the information in order to provide a sufficiently high data transfer rate between the attached device and the network.

Adding new nodes to an existing ring will temporarily affect its operation since the link must be broken to insert a new repeater. Whilst this is being done, the rest of the devices will be unable to use the ring. This can be avoided by duplicating the path.

Although it is not strictly necessary for the operation of the ring, it is commonplace to include a special device to monitor the traffic and remove packets of information which get corrupted and which would otherwise circulate without being removed or re-used. The monitor can also be used to pin-point nodes or repeaters which are not functioning correctly. To do this, any node or repeater which detects a packet with an error in it sends a special message to the monitor which can be used to work out where the error occurred. Monitors can also be used to gather statistics about the use of the network to assist in planning future developments of the system.

Bus or Highway

A bus network consists of a main highway for transporting information between the devices which are connected to it (Figure 3.9). It is a development of the data bus which is built into computer systems for interconnecting all the various components such as the processor, the memory and the peripheral controllers. The idea is that all the components in the system are connected to the same transmission medium and share in its use. In the case of a local area network, each node is given a unique address which the others use to append to the messages which they send to it. Since there is only one transmission path available in the whole network, there must be some scheme for sharing its use as fairly as possible amongst all the devices connected to it.

Many schemes can be devised for sharing the bus, ranging from each node being given a time slot in which to send information, through a frequency division system, to a completely random method in which any device can send information at any time. In all cases the nodes must be sufficiently intelligent to handle the problems which occur when the channel is already in use or when data gets corrupted by colliding with somebody else's. The data bus itself is completely passive, unlike those employed in ring networks. Each node must listen all the time to the network to detect information which is being sent to it. Also, the nodes must implement a set of high-level protocols to provide the functions of ensuring that the data received is the same as that which was sent, because the high possibility of collision with some techniques makes it very likely that information will be damaged in transit. The access method is the most important single factor in obtaining efficient use of the network.

The major techniques used in baseband, broadband, time division multiplexed and frequency division multiplexed bus systems are discussed in more detail in a later section.

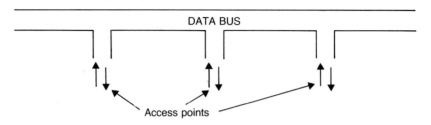

a) Conceptual Model

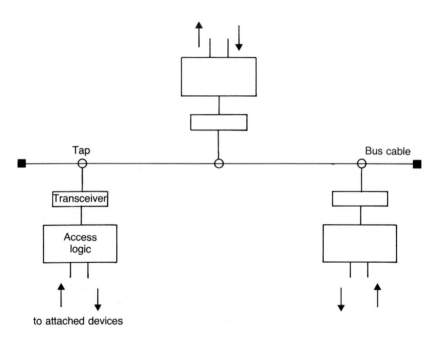

b) Practical Implementation

Figure 3.9   Data Bus Network

Other Topologies

Although any other topology is possible for a local area network, the bus and ring predominate at the present time.

A tree topology is quite commonplace. If active devices are at the points where the lines branch, the network (Figure 3.10a) can be considered as a set of interconnected stars with each device connected by a dedicated line into the network. Bus networks can often be designed as tree shapes with the branches occurring at points in the cable (Figure 3.10b).

Fully interconnected networks or meshes are sometimes required where it is important to have a lot of redundant connections, possibly to handle exceptional traffic loads or provide a high degree of security from line failure. Generally these cost significantly more to implement than would a typical local area network or even a typical star. One of the reasons given for implementing a local area network is to reduce costs by providing a shared data transmission network, and this is not generally consistent with the design aims of a mesh network.

SIGNALLING TECHNIQUES

To transmit information successfully from one location to another over a cable or other transmission medium requires the information to be coded in a manner which is suitable for the medium and information type involved. For local area networks, two classes of signalling technique are generally used: baseband and broadband.

Baseband

Baseband signalling is the simplest method which can be used and for this reason it has been adopted for many local area networks in use today. In fact baseband signalling involves no modulation at all in the normally accepted sense of the word. The digital signals on a baseband system are transmitted as discrete changes in the signals which correspond to the digital information of the incoming data. Various ways of encoding the signals onto the medium have been tried but the one which is currently accepted as the standard method for baseband systems is known as *Manchester encoding*. Others which are possible are the Miller and bi-polar techniques (references 3.1 and 3.2).

Manchester encoding is one of the simplest to implement and has one

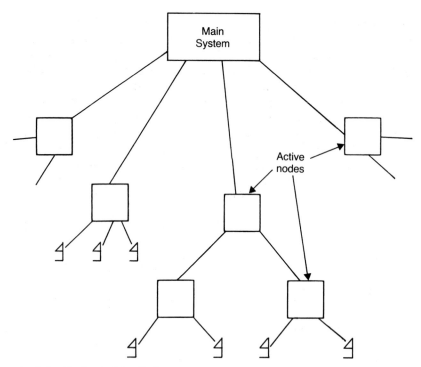

a)   Active Systems at the Nodes

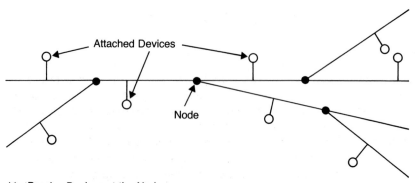

b)   Passive Devices at the Nodes

Figure 3.10   Tree Networks

feature which makes it very valuable for data communications systems: it has a built-in clocking scheme which enables every system on the network to remain in synchronisation. Manchester encoding works in the following way. The time interval is divided up into equal cells, each of which is used to represent a single bit. Each cell is itself divided in half. During the first half of the cell, the signal transmitted is the complement of the bit value being sent in that cell. In the second half of the cell, the uncomplemented value is sent. In this manner there is always a signal change during a cell, at the half-way point, which ensures that devices can be kept in synchronisation without the necessity for separate sychronisation signals. An example is useful to illustrate the process (Figure 3.11).

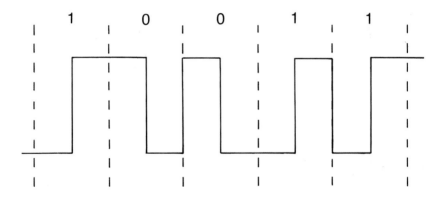

Figure 3.11 Manchester Encoding

Broadband

One of the problems with baseband signalling is that the cables can attenuate the signal below a certain level, making it difficult to determine what is noise and what is data. Over the relatively short distances involved on most local area networks which are in use today this is of little importance. For longer distances, the technique which has been employed for other computer networks has been to modulate the information onto an analogue carrier wave and to use complex modems to encode and decode the signal.

Another allied technique which has found favour with designers of local area networks has been the broadband technique which has its origins in the cable television (CATV – Community Antenna TeleVision) market. Essentially it is a method of frequency multiplexing many users onto a single cable so that in effect several channels are created. Typically a broadband system has a bandwidth of around 300 MHz so there is ample bandwidth available for data transmission services with plenty left over for other analogue-based transmission systems.

The way a broadband system works is as follows. One or two cables are used to link all the systems on the network. The two-cable system is described first.

One cable is dedicated to transmitting information and the other is dedicated to receiving. Each device is attached to both cables. The cables are run close together and one end of each is attached to a special transmitter/receiver called the HEADEND (Figure 3.12). The head-end's task is to listen to all the transmissions on the transmit cable and send them out again on the receive cable. Each device is attached to the cables through a radio frequency transmitter/receiver (RF modem) which can simultaneously listen and transmit, and which performs the interface tasks between the attached device and the cables.

The two-cable system can be adapted to use a single cable in the following manner. The available bandwidth of the cable is split into two

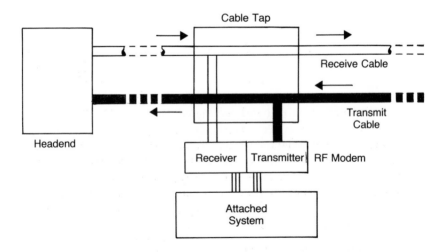

Figure 3.12   Two-Cable Broadband Bus

separate bands – say 150 MHz each. One band is allocated to information being transmitted, and the other to the reverse. Thus a system which is transmitting data uses one frequency band and this information is received on this frequency band by the headend device which retransmits it again on a different frequency this time within the receiving band. All the systems on the network listen to the receiving frequency and they accept information which is destined for them by recognising their address on the packet of data. Figure 3.13 shows the main hardware components of a single cable broadband network.

Thus a broadband system can be full-duplex in operation, since separate frequencies are used for sending and receiving.

In practice, the transmitting and receiving bands are themselves split up into a number of different channels so that many different users and services can share the same physical medium without any fear of interference with each other. The technique originally adopted using the two-cable broadband transmission was to allocate a separate channel to each pair of users. Thus a total bandwidth of 300 MHz, say, was split into a large number of channels, each with a limited bandwidth specifically suited to the application being served. On a single channel, a number of separate terminals could be used in the normal way for a multidropped line. If the transmission requirements are such that the channel cannot be

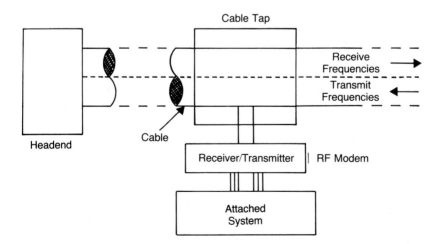

Figure 3.13   One-Cable Broadband Bus

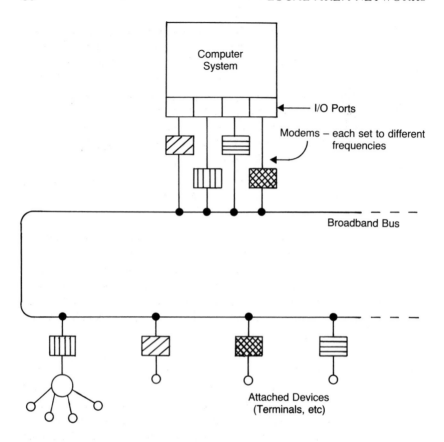

Figure 3.14   Connecting a Computer System to a Broadband Bus using Fixed Frequency Bands

shared adequately by more than one conversation, one pair of devices would be the exclusive users of it. Using this technique, channels with transmission speeds as high as the users desired could be implemented.

The major problem with this approach is where a single device, such as a mainframe computer, needs to be in dialogue with a number of other devices, possibly at the same time. The way to do this would be to install a pair of modems for each of the channels which are being used as illustrated in Figure 3.14.

The obvious disadvantage with this approach is that one pair of modems is needed for each channel and one hardware port on the mainframe computer is needed for each supported device. It prevents one device from talking to another without a lot of difficulty unless they both have modems of the same frequency. It is possible to attach multiplexers through the modems to the channel to minimise the number of modems and ports needed and to maximise the number of devices which can be supported, and this was the solution which was normally adopted.

Better alternatives could be found. Advances, both in the hardware and in the techniques used for accessing and using shared packet systems, provide the key to the greatly increased potential of the broadband network as a viable system for a local area network.

One technique which holds great potential is to allocate one or more channels (in fact pairs of channels – one for sending and one for receiving) to be buses which can be shared using one of the techniques which have been developed for time division multiplexing. With a channel bandwidth sufficient to permit a data transmission speed of a few million bits per second, it is possible for a large number of users to share a single channel without affecting the service which the user perceives.

Another technique which can be used is to employ what are known as frequency agile modems. These are standard Radio Frequency (RF) modems except for the fact that they can switch from one frequency band to another. In this way, a single device need have only one modem for it to be able to communicate at different times with a number of other devices. For each conversation the devices involved must first agree on the pair of frequencies they will use and then switch both their modems to them. This assumes that the frequencies are not being used by anybody else. A network controlling device is usually employed to allocate the frequencies to the devices wishing to be in conversation. In practice, the device which is initiating the conversation asks the controller if the device it wishes to send to is in a position to receive information. The controller checks the availability of the other device and, if it is free, informs it that someone wishes to communicate with it and tells it which frequency to use. The controller also informs the initiator of the conversation which frequency to switch his modem to. That frequency band is then allocated solely to that conversation for its duration.

The modems which are needed to connect a piece of equipment are essentially VHF transmitters and receivers which use two separate frequencies to transmit and receive. Rather than transmitting using an aerial as would a normal transmitter, these modems use the coaxial cable. With present-day technology, RF modems which can support a data transmission rate of around 19 kbps are readily available using the modulation techniques normally associated with data transmission over standard telephone lines. RF modems which can operate at much higher rates of around 2 Mbps and which require a bandwidth of 6 MHz can also be obtained. It is these special modems and the fact that a special device is needed to translate all signals from the transmit frequency band to the receive band that put up the cost of the broadband system.

The system is very well suited to carrying analogue signals such as telephone traffic and, more especially, television signals. Thus a broadband network can devote some of its channels to carrying computer-generated information, and other channels to analogue signals including real-time colour video. This is totally beyond the capabilities of most other local area network systems.

Standard cable television line amplifiers can be used to give a long range to the network. A cable length of many kilometres is possible without noticeable degradation of the signal, but if a broadcast bus is implemented on one of the channels which is operating in a contention mode, then the access algorithm and the length of the packet of information could severely limit the practical length of the cable.

The cable used for cable television and hence for broadband networks is similar, but not identical to, conventional coaxial cable. It exhibits a high immunity to interference so that it can be run in electrically hostile environments. Special tools are available to enable the cable to be tapped without cutting it or severely damaging it or interfering with the transmissions it is carrying at the time. Some doubt has been expressed about the reliability of these devices and some suppliers prefer to cut the cable and make a normal connection.

EXTRA INTELLIGENCE NEEDED

A shared transmission such as a local area network requires conventions which all users must follow. In the case of the traditional type of computer network based on a central computer, the conventions are those imposed by the central device itself and by the rules set for using any intermediate network such as the public telephone system. A local area network is constrained to use only those rules which it sets itself since it is located on only one site and is solely under the control of a single organisation. However, the way the network is used needs to be as closely defined as for any other network, since it is shared by everybody.

The standard diagram of a local area network connection (Figure 3.1) illustrates the major pieces of hardware and software involved in providing a connection. The diagram is idealised and in some real networks some of the functions may be combined into one black box or piece of software, or even omitted altogether. Their relative importance in the different types of local area networking technologies is also different. The diagram merely indicates the sort of functions one should expect.

The cable tap is a piece of hardware which is used to obtain an electrical connection to the transmission medium. In the case of a wire cable, it is usually a tee-piece or a tapping device which makes electrical contact with all the relevant conductors in the cable. For an optical fibre, the tapping device is something which performs the dual function of converting the light signals into electrical signals and also regenerating the light pulses for continued transmission along the fibre.

The transceiver which is connected to the cable tap exists to put the signals onto the cable in a form which is suitable for onward transmission, and for reading the signals off the medium itself. The transceiver is given the information to transmit in the form of a string of digital signals which it has to convert into the appropriate form. If the signal is modulated, it is this device which provides the modem function. Careful attention to the details of the interface can do much to ensure that the network as a whole is reliable and is unaffected by the operation or failure of the attached device. Reliability of the transceiver is especially important in ring systems in which it is an active part of the transmission system, failure of which can cause the whole network to be unusable unless alternative routes are provided.

The cable transceiver requires an additional piece of hardware to decide if the information which is being received is destined for that station or if it should be ignored. This hardware must contain some software in order that the decision can be made. Each station on the network is known by a unique name so that messages can be addressed to it by the other users of the system. When a message is assembled for transmission to another user, its network address is attached to each packet which is transmitted. Every transceiver in the network receives the message and each one passes it on to the next piece of hardware and software to decide whether this message is intended for that station or not. If it is, the message is passed on to the next higher piece of logic, the host-to-network interface.

The device which is using the local area network may be anything from a very simple terminal to a full mainframe computer. Each type of attached device is likely to have a different type of interface built into it. Simple terminals which are designed to be attached to a computer or a terminal controller over local links are most likely to use a simple bit serial interface for either coaxial or twisted-pair cable. An intelligent device may have a much more sophisticated interface which is capable of putting the information into packets suitable for transmission over long distances. Other devices may normally be interconnected by means of a parallel bus ribbon cable. The format of the message to be transmitted on the local area network must be the same for all the users of it, regardless of their individual characteristics, so a piece of hardware or software must be incorporated into the system to provide the conversion from the format of the output from the attached device into that required for onward transmission on the network. Exactly what this device does and how it performs its functions depend on such factors as the nature of the attached device and the type of network being used.

4 Network Sharing Techniques

INTRODUCTION

In the previous chapter the basic components of local area networks were described. However, more than just a few lengths of wire and some modems are required to make a network operate. Methods of using the network must be devised to make it suitable for carrying data.

As we have seen, networks with the same topology can be used in several different ways and can use different media to effect interconnection. Thus, neither the topology nor the medium are wholly suitable as a method of classifying local area networks. It is much better to approach the problem through the way the network operates and the access and control procedures which have to be followed to make it operate as desired, although even here the same method may be applicable to several different topologies and applications. However, a classification based on the access and control methods is the one which is most relevant to the products and research systems in existence today. It also serves to illustrate a number of important features of local area network technology.

Some of the techniques described here are of general applicability and others are relevant only to a particular type of configuration. The type of network which is the most relevant to the method being described is identified.

MULTIPLEXING TECHNIQUES

The idea behind multiplexing is to enable more than one user of a single circuit or network to make use of it without interfering significantly with the other users. Many techniques have been tried for multiplexing but only those which are particularly useful for local area networks will be considered here.

Multiplexing differs from concentration in that the devices which use concentrators contend with each other to use the output circuit. Multiplexers, on the other hand, share a high-speed line amongst a number of lower-speed devices. The distinction between multiplexers and concentrators used to be clear-cut but now, with the introduction of intelligence into multiplexers and the use of statistical techniques for sharing the circuit, the difference is much less marked.

Time Division Multiplexing

Consider the situation which is illustrated in Figure 4.1. A number of relatively slow devices each want to use a circuit to another device. Usually the other device is at a distance away from the cluster of low-speed devices and it makes economic sense to share a long line amongst as many users as possible. The example is typical of a group of terminals which are located in one site, all using a computer in another location and requiring the provision of one or more leased lines between the two locations.

The cost of providing each low-speed device with a separate leased line would be prohibitively high, so multiplexing is used to share the relatively expensive high-speed resource. This is parallel to the situation of a local area network where economical interconnection can be achieved by means of sharing the data transmission network amongst all the devices connected to the system.

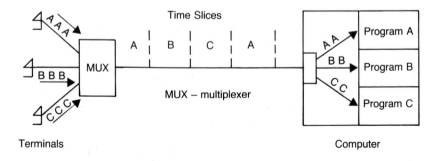

Figure 4.1   Line-Sharing by Low-Speed Devices

The multiplexer in the diagram allocates each of the attached devices a time slot for them to have exclusive use of the shared high-speed circuit. Information flows between the end devices and the multiplexer at a steady rate determined by the end devices themselves and not by the multiplexer. The time slots allocated to each device are kept fairly small in order that each device can have frequent use of the shared circuit, at the same time minimising the amount of buffer storage required in the multiplexer itself. The data which passes along the shared circuit is a more or less continuous stream of binary digits or characters. To unscramble this at the other end requires the presence of a reverse multiplexer which is synchronised with the multiplexer and which can then divide up the incoming data stream into individual data streams corresponding to the ones produced by the devices at the other end.

Time division multiplexing is an important technique for a number of local area network technologies, especially those based on the ring topology. In rings, each station is normally given the opportunity to use the ring for a fixed period of time. Normally no actual physically separate multiplexer is used, since the mechanisms for accessing the ring, which are built into the repeaters, are inherently time division multiplexing techniques.

Statistical Time Division Multiplexing

Using normal time division multiplexing techniques, channel capacity is wasted unless every device is transmitting data all the time, and this is unlikely to be the case in a practical situation. If time slots could be allocated only when they are actually required by the devices connected to the mulitplexer, then a much better utilisation of the capacity of the shared channel could be achieved. This is the idea behind statistical time division multiplexing (STDM).

The devices which are connected to the STDM multiplexer actually contend for use of the shared circuit. The multiplexer is a complicated device which has enough intelligence to allocate the channel efficiently to the devices connected to it. Statistically it is unlikely that all the devices served by the multiplexer will be active at the same instant in time, so an STDM system can be made to serve a larger number of devices than can a multiplexer using ordinary TDM methods.

Local area networks which rely on contention to allocate the network, such as those employing the carrier sensing techniques described later, are essentially STDM methods, since the time slots on the network are

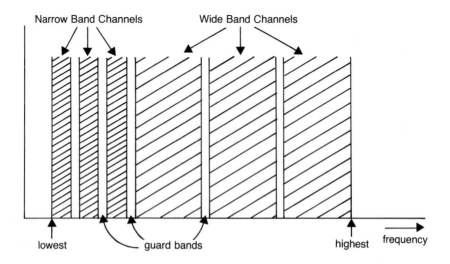

Figure 4.2   Frequency Division Multiplexing

allocated on demand from the devices connected to the network. Like local area networks which use standard time division multiplexing techniques, the intelligence needed to perform the multiplexing is distributed around to every device on the network and is inherent in the access mechanism involved.

Frequency Division Multiplexing

Every transmission channel has a certain frequency bandwidth (ie the difference between the highest and the lowest frequency which can be transmitted successfully). If the bandwidth is sufficiently wide, it can be split into a number of bands which can each carry a smaller frequency band than that of the original channel and whose aggregate bandwidth is less than or equal to it. Each of the individual channels may still have sufficient bandwidth to be able to transport information at an adequate speed for many purposes.

The way the bandwidth is split up is shown in Figure 4.2 which is a graph of frequency plotted against signal. As can be seen, the individual channels need to be separated from their neighbours by a narrower band in order that the data being carried by one channel does not interfere with

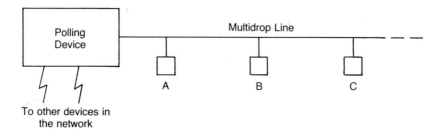

Figure 4.3 A Polled System on One Line

that being carried by the adjacent channels. These bands which separate the information-carrying bands are called *Guard Bands*.

Using the technique of frequency division multiplexing, a number of information channels with low bandwidth requirements can share the wide bandwidth provided by some transmission media.

Polling

Polling is not normally considered to be a multiplexing technique although it is a well understood method of sharing one communication circuit amongst several devices which do not need to transmit continuously. Consider the simple situation illustrated in Figure 4.3.

The devices labelled A, B, C, . . . are connected by the same circuit to the controlling device, which may be a computer or just a terminal controller. If all the devices tried to transmit at the same instant and there were no method of deciding which was to have priority, the signals which would appear on the circuit would be incomprehensible. The normal solution to the problem is for the controlling device to ask each of the devices on the circuit whether they have any data to send and, if they have, to let them have exclusive use of the circuit to transmit their message. Various systems of priority can be used to allow those devices which need to transmit information more often than the others to be given the opportunity to use the circuit more often. Each device knows which requests are directed to it by means of a unique address which is placed at the head of each message.

Incoming data is handled in a similar way by the controller adding the address of the destination device to the message before it transmits the

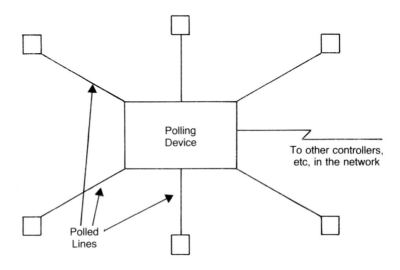

Figure 4.4   Star Polling System

message on the circuit. The target device recognises its own address and reads in the message.

Polling is also frequently used for centrally controlled systems of the type illustrated in Figure 4.4. The device at the centre of the star could be a computer system or a controller serving a computer system which is incapable of handling more than one message to or from one device at a time. In this situation, the end devices are each allowed to have exclusive use of the controller or computer rather than the communications medium as in the previous example.

Polling is a technique which is more often associated with a computer system or a concentrator which is serving a number of low-usage terminals.

BROADCAST BUS-SHARING TECHNIQUES

A broadcast bus can conveniently be thought of as a single data transmission channel to which all the systems on the network are listening all the time. A message from any one user of the bus to any other is 'broadcast' in the same way as a radio message is broadcast on the airwaves for anybody with the right sort of receiver to be able to listen to. In the context of local area networks, the airwaves are generally replaced by a physical cable of some sort, generally an electrical cable or an optic fibre link, although there is no reason, other than privacy requirements and the fear of interference, to prevent the use of radio broadcast for local area networks if this is suitable for the application.

The other main feature of a bus is that it is shared by every user on the system. In order to share the use of a broadcast bus in a local area network, it is necessary to devise a method by which each user is given a fair chance of being able to transmit information. More than one user is unable to send information at a time, since to do so on a broadcast medium would mean that the messages would become intermingled and the result would be indecipherable. One possibility is to allocate time slots to each of the users during which they have exclusive use of the network.

Another alternative is for each user just to transmit his messages as and when they are ready and if someone else is using the medium at that time to retransmit the messages which collide. The last mentioned method has been tried but it was found that, in its basic form, it made poor use of the available transmission capacity, especially when there was a large amount of traffic on the network and the likelihood of a collision was very high.

The solution usually adopted for current systems is that in which each user contends with the others in order to obtain exclusive use of the medium. If someone else is using the network, they do not attempt to transmit. In the relatively rare instances of two users trying to transmit at the same instant, both users involved should cease transmission and make another attempt at a later time.

Whichever solution is chosen, since all the systems using the network must listen to every transmission, a comprehensive addressing scheme is required. Also, in order that the network is fair to everyone, a set of rules must be devised which all the users must observe. It is quite possible that one unscrupulous user who knows that everyone else is abiding by the rules could gain an unfair proportion of the available capacity by deliberately not following them.

It may appear at first sight that allowing each user to contend for exclusive use of the network is liable to cause problems, since collisions may be expected to occur frequently, which would result in two or more messages being corrupted. However, by careful design of the access algorithms, combined with rapid transmission and access logic speeds, we can achieve a high degree of efficiency.

Efficiency can be measured as a percentage of the transmission capacity of the network which is actually used, ie if the network has a raw transmission rate of 10 Mbps, and this is capable of transporting 9 Mbps of information without errors, then it can be said to be 90% efficient. But, in the ridiculous situation, this may be the same data stream over and over again, or control information being transmitted continuously, whilst end-user devices are trying to place their data on the network but are unable to gain access.

Possibly the best measure of efficiency is the ratio of information transported successfully by the network to that offered to it for transmission.

We must, therefore, be careful in deciding exactly how the efficiency of the network is quoted, as the method used to calculate it can produce very different results. In the case of most broadcast bus systems which rely on contention to allocate the network to the users, the quoted efficiency can only be the statistical average and could be much better or worse under certain circumstances. It is not impossible that every user on the network will attempt to transmit at the same instant, so causing the loss of every message, but it is statistically unlikely.

In common with other data communication techniques in use today, local area networks based on broadcast buses typically use packets to send the information. A message is split up into a number of separate blocks and each is transmitted separately with a certain amount of extra information placed in headers and trailers. This is similar in concept to the frame which is now the standard mechanism used for data transmission. The format of a typical packet or frame is shown in Figure 4.5.

The header of a normal packet includes the addresses of the node which is sending the data and the node to which it is being sent, information about the packet itself (eg whether it contains data or is a control packet), the length of the data field, etc. The trailer usually contains a special field (field check sequence) which is examined by the destination node to see if the packet has been damaged in transit, and another field which indicates the end of the packet. The advantages of packet formatting are associated with the detection and correction of erroneous infor-

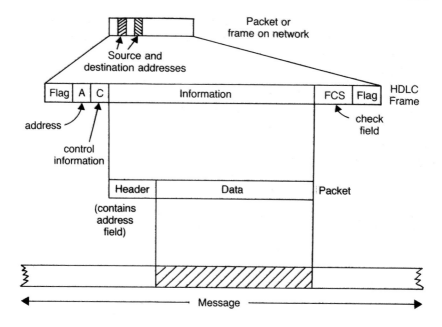

Figure 4.5 Typical Packet Format

mation, and with the fact that any arrangement of data can be sent without fear that it would be interpreted as a control field.

Whenever a packet is received by the destination node, the error detection fields are examined and the information contained in it is compared with that calculated by the destination node itself using the known algorithm. If the two differ, the destination node can transmit a special packet back to the source node telling it that a certain packet has been incorrectly received and requesting retransmission of it. The source node need only retransmit the erroneous packet and not the whole message.

The length of the packet can be chosen to suit the characteristics of the transmission medium, the devices using the network or the network itself. Generally the choice is a compromise between the length which is most likely to be transported without error, the time which is needed to place the packet on the network, and the amount of usable information contained in it in proportion to the rather large overheads imposed by the header and trailer information fields. Packets generally used for broadcast bus systems are variable in length with a maximum of around 8000 - 10,000 bits.

The other major advantage of the packet format for data transmission is the freedom it gives the user in the choice of characters. Older data transmission techniques used to intersperse the data characters with characters which were used to control the device at the other end of the link. Thus, if the character stream which was being sent included some of these control characters, special precautions had to be taken otherwise the device at the other end would do things which the sender did not request. Usually the sender would check for the known control characters, and when they occurred would replace them with another character sequence which would be recognised at the other end where the device would replace it with the one which was originally intended. Packetising the data effectively overcomes this problem since the data is enclosed inside a set of header and trailer fields which have a fixed format and serve to delimit the data field as well as define its length.

In a broadcast bus system, every user is attached to the same circuit, so each must have its own unique address on the network. Packets include in their header field the addresses of both the sender and the destination. Thus, when a packet is transmitted onto the network, each node connected to it examines the destination address field to see if the packet is intended for itself. If it is, then it reads it into its internal storage where it takes the action it feels is appropriate. If the destination address is that of another node, it ignores it. This is another reason why the packet format for data transmission on a broadcast system is so useful since it is impossible to tell the source of a message merely by looking to see which wire the data came along.

The techniques most commonly encountered for broadcast bus local area networks will be examined below and their major features explained. It is inappropriate at this stage to discuss exactly how each of the techniques is implemented in practice since one single technique can use an infinite number of packet formats and access algorithms. Such considerations are best left to the descriptions of the products themselves which can be obtained from the suppliers. General descriptions can be found in reference 4.1.

ALOHA

The ALOHA techniques for using a broadcast medium are those which were used in what was probably the first of the broadcast packet networks to be implemented. It is now mainly of historical interest only in the context of local area networks, since the technique is not efficient enough to be used for them, although it does have the virtue of simplicity. However, it has proved such a great influence on the subsequent design of local area networks that it should be discussed as it does throw some light on the way the techniques have evolved.

The University of Hawaii computer centre is based at Honolulu, although it serves a large number of terminals scattered around many of the islands in the Hawaiian group. To provide an easy method of access from these widespread terminals to the central computer centre, a radio broadcast medium was used. Naturally this medium is accessible to everybody with the right equipment and it uses the so-called 'luminiferous ether' through which all electromagnetic radiation was once thought to pass. Therefore, packet broadcasting was the first choice from the points of view of reliability (ie the likelihood of damaged packets through noise is very high), and the need to employ an addressing mechanism. The ALOHA methods come in two main types (Pure ALOHA and Slotted ALOHA), although other methods have been experimented with.

Pure ALOHA was the first attempt to set up a usable packet broadcast system on the Hawaiian islands. Described simply, each device on the network has a transmitter and, whenever that device has sufficient data to send, it places it in a packet, together with the source and destination address, and then transmits it. On transmission it starts a timer which is used to determine whether or not the packet has reached its destination successfully or been lost or damaged on the way. If another node is transmitting at the same instant, the airways will carry two packets at the same time and the two packets will be corrupted. The receiving nodes will detect errors in the packets by means of the field check sequences not matching the rest of the packet. They will not acknowledge receipt of the packets.

The amount of time lost in the transmission due to overlapping packets is illustrated in Figure 4.6. Even though there may have been only a very small amount of overlap, the whole of two packets are lost and must be retransmitted.

When the sender of a packet does not receive an acknowledgement, it is assumed that the packet must be retransmitted. To avoid the possibility of the same two devices which were involved in the original collision

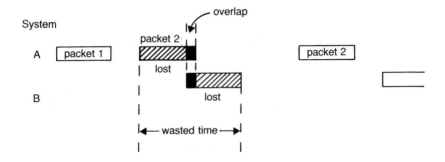

Figure 4.6   ALOHA Packet Broadcasting

broadcasting at the same time again, the time-out used by each transmitter on the network is random and will therefore usually be different for each device.

Provided that there is relatively little traffic on the network and the packets used are fairly small, then the technique is reasonably good. The bandwidth is high but the propagation times are significant so there is a very high chance that packets will collide. Also, even when two packets collide, the transmitters have no way of detecting this so they continue transmitting until the whole of the packet is gone. Naturally this is wasteful of the bandwidth. Typically the Pure ALOHA technique gives an efficiency of around 18.4% of the available bandwidth.

One way of improving the efficiency is to remove some of the freedom which is part of the Pure ALOHA technique. The discipline which is imposed by the *Slotted ALOHA* method is to allow the devices to transmit only at specified times and not whenever they want to. The time is divided up into intervals and the transmitters are only allowed to transmit at the beginning of each time frame or slot. Due account is taken of the time it takes for the transmissions to reach the central computer site in Honolulu so that, regardless of the distance between it and the transmitting sites, the packets all reach Honolulu at the same time. Apart from this, no other discipline is imposed on the users of the network. Thus more than one user may start transmitting packets at around the same time and they will still transmit them in full even though they will be corrupted in transit, but the amount of time between the start of the 'first' packet to be transmitted

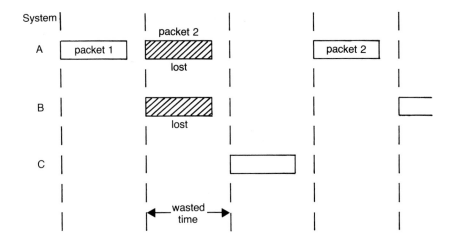

Figure 4.7   Slotted ALOHA

and the end of the 'last' will be the length of the longest packet, which will
be shorter in almost every case than that experienced in the Pure
ALOHA system (Figure 4.7).

The Slotted ALOHA technique gives a much better use of the available bandwidth: typically 36.8% for large populations of users. Small
populations achieve much better figures.

Reservation

Reservation is a blanket term applied to techniques which ensure that the
broadcast medium is reserved solely for the use of one node on the
network. There are many ways of reserving the network but in this section
we will consider just those most commonly used for local area networks at
the present time.

Time Slots

The network resource can be shared amongst several users by allocating
to each one a time slot of their own during which only they can transmit
information. This is a standard time division multiplexing technique and
was considered in some detail earlier.

Polling

Another way that the network can be shared amongst several users is for some controlling device to ask the other devices on the network if they have any data to send. In other words, each device is polled. Polling requires that special blocks of data are sent to each of the devices in turn, which takes up valuable bandwidth, although this is not usually too important in a local area network. More importantly the central controller must always be working and it must know every device on the network, making it difficult for new devices to be added as and when they are required.

Daisy-Chaining

Daisy-chaining is a generic term to describe the technique of passing control from one device to the next. Sometimes this is achieved by means of separate circuits from those used to carry the data, and in other cases the same wires are used with special packets to pass control. The most relevant technique under this heading for local area networks is that known as Token Passing which is considered separately in the following paragraph.

Token Passing

One way of reserving the medium is by means of a control token, which is a special packet of information which itself conveys no information but enables the holder of it to have exclusive use of the medium without fear of interruption from anyone else. The most important requirement of this technique is to ensure that each user of the network is given the token in turn. For this reason token passing is especially useful for ring topologies where it is easy to ensure that the token is passed from one node to the next because data always passes sequentially around the network. Token passing will be discussed in more detail in the section on rings. In this section the particular features of token passing in broadcast bus networks will be considered.

In a broadcast network, every node can hear every transmission made by every other node and so the token must be explicitly addressed to the next node which is to have control. Generally the nodes on the bus are arranged logically in a ring although their physical arrangement can be quite different. Not all the nodes need to be able to transmit but instead can just listen to the transmission on the network, in which case they will not be included in the logical ring for the passing of the token although they can have normal data packets addressed to them. A typical arrangement of a bus using a token access is shown in Figure 4.8.

The logical arrangement of the nodes on a bus can be changed at any time and in fact a single node can be included more than once per circulation round the 'ring' if it is necessary to give it rather higher priority. Provided that the individual nodes are sufficiently intelligent, it is easy to alter the configuration to take account of nodes which fail.

The operation of the token passing bus is as follows. When a node has a packet ready to send, it waits until it is passed a packet containing the control token by another node. It then transmits its packet of information to the network until either the whole message is gone or until the preset time interval allowed for each node to have the token expires. It then transmits the token, usually to the next node in the logical ring. However,

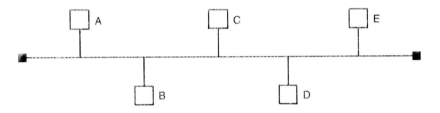

a)   Physical Arrangement

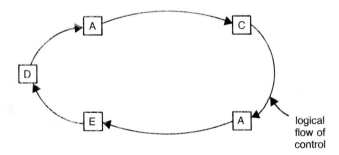

b)   Logical Arrangement (B can only listen)

Figure 4.8   Token Passing on a Bus

in some implementations it may be permitted to request an immediate response from the node to which the message was just sent, in which case the token is sent to that node rather than the next one in the sequence. The destination node must then respond immediately with an acknowledgement packet back to the original sender. The token is then passed on to the next node in the sequence.

The token could be part of the information packet which the node transmits. Since every user of the network hears every packet which is transmitted, the same packet can serve two purposes simultaneously: to pass information to another node, and to pass control to the next one in sequence.

Contention Techniques

Another popular way of sharing the use of the medium in a broadcast system is to employ a scheme for obtaining exclusive use of the medium in contention with the other users of the network as and when required. The success of contention networks depends to a very large extent on the design of the algorithms for detecting that the network is free or in use and stopping transmission if there is a collision between two packets broadcast at the same time. By careful design, a very high efficiency can be achieved. Broadcast contention buses are especially useful for networks where the nodes send out information in bursts, since to allocate each one of them a time slot would generally be wasteful when most of the devices would have no data ready to send at that instant.

Carrier Sense Multiple Access (CSMA)

The term Carrier Sense Multiple Access needs explaining before the technical details of how the method is made to work are presented. By Carrier Sense is meant that before accessing the transmission medium to send a message, each device first listens to it to establish if there is a carrier signal present indicating that someone else is already using the network. Multiple Access is used to indicate that a number of users all share the same transmission resource. So, with a CSMA network all the users share the same circuits and each one listens to it all the time so that it does not try to transmit when someone else is using the network. Using this technique the likelihood of two or more data packets colliding is reduced but not eliminated. It is sometimes known by the descriptive title *Listen Before Transmission*. CSMA was first proposed in 1971 in a paper published by the University of Hawaii.

Even though each user tries to avoid transmitting at the same time as the others on the network by listening for a gap in the transmission, it is possible that two users who are simultaneously waiting whilst an earlier transmission is completed will sense that the medium is quiet at the same instant and both start transmitting. After a certain period, which is determined by the time it takes a signal to propagate from one device to the other, both of the packets will start to overlap and the information they contain will become corrupted.

In the basic CSMA which we are considering now the nodes which are transmitting will continue doing so until all of the packet has been put on the network even though it will have to be retransmitted later when a positive acknowledgement from the recipient is not received. At some point later on, the nodes will again try to send the packets.

This form of CSMA is sometimes called *non-persistent* and *unslotted:* non-persistent because the nodes do not retry immediately the network is quiet, and unslotted because each node transmits outside a network time frame rather like the Pure ALOHA system. Like the ALOHA technique, CSMA can be improved by using a network enforced time frame in which every node is only allowed to transmit at the start of specified time slots. This does not overcome the possibility of collisions occurring, but it does reduce the time wasted on the network whilst overlapping packets are being transmitted. This version of CSMA is called *slotted non-persistent CSMA*.

Persistent CSMA

In the persistent version of CSMA, the nodes which are trying to retransmit a packet which has been damaged in transit try again fairly quickly after the channel becomes idle.

If the nodes try immediately the channel becomes idle, then the method is called 1-persistent. In this method, each node listens until the channel is idle and then transmits straight away. This avoids the channel being unnecessarily idle, but it is unsatisfactory in practice since if two nodes are waiting to retry at the same time, they will both start transmitting as soon as the channel becomes idle and so the packets will collide again.

Persistent CSMA is easily modified to overcome this problem. Instead of retrying immediately, the nodes retry only with a certain probability p. In other words, persistent CSMA in which all nodes retry immediately is where the probability is set to one. In the case where the probability is less than one, and n nodes are waiting to retransmit in a p-persistent CSMA system, n.p nodes will try to retransmit as soon as the channel becomes idle. Unless the network is heavily loaded, it is unlikely that very many nodes will be waiting to retry at any instant, so the possibility of a collision is reduced.

Analyses have been made of persistent CSMA which show that a slotted 1-persistent CSMA system is about 53% efficient whereas an optimised p-persistent system can have an efficiency as high as 82%.

Carrier Sense Multiple Access with Collision Detection (CSMA/CD)

The development of the CSMA technique which is now the one most commonly used in most current local area networks is the one known as CSMA/CD, where CD stands for Collision Detection. This means that the nodes listen to the network at the same time as they are transmitting, so that if a collision does occur, this can be detected as soon as it happens and the transmission can be abandoned as soon as possible, so saving transmission time on the network. In this kind of technique there is no need to have specific acknowledgement packets since the transmitter can actually hear if a collision is happening. CSMA/CD is also sometimes known as *Listen Whilst Transmitting* as well as listening before. The main advantage is that time is not wasted transmitting information which will have to be retransmitted because it will not reach its destination unharmed (see Figure 4.9). The channel time also saved is thus made available for others to use. Collisions can only occur during the interval shortly after a transmission is started and before the signal has had time to reach all the nodes on the network. This is called the collision window.

Naturally, for the technique to work properly, each node which detects that its packet has collided with another should not attempt to retransmit immediately, otherwise the same packets will just collide again. The technique which is usually adopted to avoid this problem is for each station which detects a collision to immediately transmit a burst of noise in order that all the other transmitting stations can hear the collision and then to wait for a random interval of time before attempting to retransmit. If, on retrying, the medium is busy or another collision occurs, the station backs off for a longer period of time. In this way the nodes using the network adapt themselves to the loading of the medium. When it is lightly loaded, the retrying nodes will usually find the medium quiet and

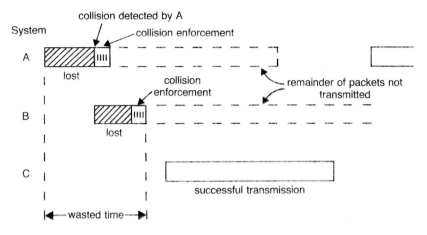

Figure 4.9   CSMA/CD

so the waiting time between transmissions will be at a minimum. As the loading increases, so the waiting time will also increase so that the number of collisions will not rise too high as would be the case if the average period before retrying was constant.

By means of careful design of the algorithms for retrying and backing off, it is possible to achieve an efficiency in the use of the bandwidth of over 90%.

As mentioned earlier, no explicit acknowledgement packets are required since the transmitting station can itself detect if a packet collides with another. If a packet is damaged by some other means, the receiving node will normally be able to detect this by examining the error check fields in the packet. It is then the responsibility of the destination node to request retransmission by means of a special packet which says in effect that the packet was received in error. If the destination node is not working, the sending node will not receive any response at all, so a higher level protocol is normally used between the nodes so that a sending node must first determine by means of an exchange of packets that the destination node is there and is in a fit state to receive information.

Carrier Sense Multiple Access with Collision Avoidance (CSMA/CA)

CSMA/CA is not such a widely known technique as CSMA/CD, although they do share a number of features. CSMA/CA is essentially a combination of normal slotted time division multiplexing and CSMA/CD. It operates in the following manner.

At the end of each transmission, the time is divided into time slots which are allocated to each of the nodes on the network. The node which has the first time slot transmits a packet of information if it has one available. After it is finished, the next node in the priority order is given the next time slot. If any node does not have any packets ready to send then that time slot remains unused. If all the nodes are unready to transmit when their appointed time slot is reached, then after they have all been given the opportunity once, the network reverts to the normal CSMA/CD mode of operation; in other words each node contends with the others for use of the communication channel. Once the channel has been used again to transmit a packet, the system switches back to the time slots.

Normally there is an extra priority given to certain of the nodes so that they are given the first time slots of any sequence. Once theirs have been offered and have not been used, the rest are allocated in rotation. The technique is claimed to be very efficient, especially in networks where some nodes need to use the network more often than others and where the overall loading is fairly high. It should be obvious that the technique can only work well if the nodes attached to the network contain a reasonable amount of intelligence because of the time slot synchronisation and allocation algorithms required, as well as the normal CSMA/CD access methods which themselves require intelligence.

RING ACCESS TECHNIQUES

Local area networks which are arranged in the form of a ring generally require a different type of access mechanism because of the fundamentally different way in which control of the medium is passed from one node to another. In a bus network every node on that network hears every message which is transmitted by every other node more or less at the time it is transmitted with only a very small delay introduced by the propagation time in the medium. In the case of a ring, the direction of flow of information is always the same and information packets are passed from one node to the next in the ring. Generally the control of the medium also passes along the ring in the same manner as the data. This unidirectional flow of data and control means that a completely different set of access techniques can be devised and, in some cases, far less intelligence is needed in the devices which are actually attached to the network: ie the transceivers or repeaters.

A loop can be thought of as a kind of ring but generally the difference is in the way the two are controlled. A loop usually has a single device whose task it is to decide which of the other nodes is to be allowed to transmit information at each instant. This may be achieved by means of polling the devices in some preset order or by sending out an empty packet which is available for anybody to use.

The packets of information used in a ring are always passed from one node to the next, after having been regenerated by the node repeater. Unlike a bus system where each packet disappears naturally from the network as the signal dies away, the information circulating on a ring must be removed explicitly by a node. Usually the node which originates the packet is the one which is made responsible for removing it since only it is in a position to know what it has put on the network. The destination node is not usually made responsible for this, since there is no guarantee that it will be available and working.

It has been found necessary to include a special-purpose node which has the task of removing packets which are damaged in transit and have become unrecognisable to the originator. This node is generally called a *Monitor station*. It must be working all the time that the network is being used but it can be made to perform other functions as well as removing damaged packets. For example, most rings require at the start of their operation that one node generates the first packet which will be empty. The monitor station is ideally suited to do this task and at the same time to check that the ring is complete by looking for its return. The monitor station can also monitor the number of packets which are in error during operation of the network and it can detect when a node or repeater is producing a higher than normal number of erroneous packets.

All ring access techniques can be thought of as time division multiplexing methods as they effectively divide up the available bandwidth amongst the users of the network. They generally give every node a fair chance to use the network and do not rely on chance to enable everyone to get access even when the system is highly loaded.

Some ring-based products employ more than one data transmission channel to provide a degree of resilience to link and repeater failure. This naturally makes the design of the repeaters much more complicated since there will then be more than one path between devices, and in some cases the physical order of the nodes on the ring may be different on the two paths. However, the details of these are better left until the descriptions of the individual products (reference 4.2).

The following are descriptions of some of the ring access techniques that are met with most frequently. Many other methods have been tried or proposed at one time or another.

Fixed Slot

For each node on the ring, a packet is allocated for its exclusive use. All the packets circulate around the ring continuously and whenever a node has a message to send, it places it in the appropriate packet for the destination node. The destination node reads the packet after it has travelled around the ring and has been relayed untouched by every other node.

This technique is not used very often and no examples of it exist outside the research laboratories.

Pre-Allocated

A pre-allocated scheme works by dividing the time interval up into slots. Each user is allowed to transmit only during his pre-allocated slot. This technique is inefficient except in the case where the network is heavily loaded and each user is sending out information in a steady stream. Such a technique is not used now that more efficient techniques, such as empty slot, register insertion and token passing, have been developed.

Empty Slot

In the empty slot method of using a ring, one or more packets circulate continuously around the ring which can be either in use or empty. If a node has data to send then it waits until it gets an empty packet passed to it at which point it puts its data in it, the address of the destination node, its own address, and then switches a marker to flag the packet as 'in use'. This packet is then passed from one node repeater to the next until it reaches the node with the address given in the destination address field. The node repeater at this location reads the packet into its internal storage, switches a marker to indicate that the packet has been received by the destination node, and passes the packet on to the next node repeater in the ring. The packet is then passed on from node to node until it returns to the node which sent it. This node recognises it as the one it sent out by means of the address field and so it switches the 'used/unused' marker to flag the packet as now available for others to use. In general it is not permitted for the same node to reuse the packet which it sent out immediately since this would enable a single node to hog the network and would not give the other users of it a fair chance.

Thus the sending node has exclusive use of a packet for the time it takes that packet to do a complete circuit of the ring. The opportunity to use that packet is then passed to the next node. If the ring only employs one packet which is continuously circulating and each node is waiting to send data, each one will be able to use the packet in turn and there will be no chance that one node will have more turns with it than any other. This is the way that time division multiplexing works on a ring which operates using the empty slot technique. The operation of the empty slot ring is shown diagrammatically (Figure 4.10).

Empty slot rings almost always need a monitor station to spot and remove defective packets which are not flagged as empty by their originator. The monitor normally keeps a copy of every packet as it passes through it and so if the identical packet passes by more than once or twice it assumes that it is in error and so removes it and regenerates a fresh empty one.

If a destination device is not working, the repeater at that address will not flag the packet as having been received, so the sending node will know that the data has not been read.

One technique sometimes used to detect errors and repeaters or stations which are failing is for each repeater to check the parity of each packet which it relays, as well as those which are addressed to it or which it originates. If a packet which is in error is relayed, the repeater uses the next empty packet which it receives to send an error message to the monitor station. The monitor station can then use the error messages it receives to pinpoint the place where the error occurred and if it is consistently in the same place the person monitoring the system can take appropriate action. Before passing on a defective packet a repeater usually resets the parity so that error messages about the same packet are not sent by every repeater which it passes through.

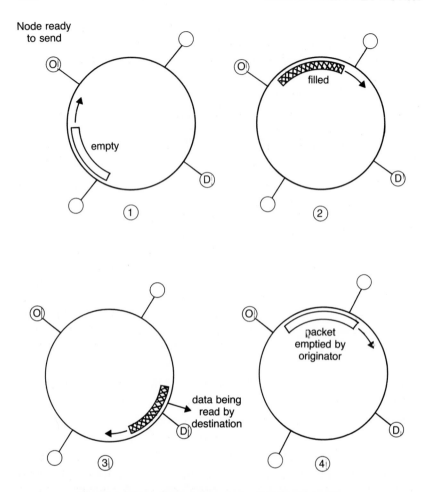

Figure 4.10   Operation of an Empty Slot Ring

Since the empty slot method of using rings reached a high state of development in the Cambridge University Computer Laboratory system it has come to be known as the Cambridge Ring. Strictly speaking the Cambridge Ring is a particular version of the empty slot technique in which a particular format of the packet is used, as shown in a later chapter. The Cambridge Ring also uses two twisted pairs of cable to transmit the data and to provide power for the repeaters. Later versions of the Cambridge Ring have used different packet lengths and formats as well as different methods of transporting the data around the ring.

Register or Buffer Insertion

To implement the register insertion technique of ring access requires that the repeaters include a buffer which can be switched in and out of the circuit as and when required. This buffer is usually a shift register, hence the use of the alternative title.

When a node has a message to send, it places it in the appropriate packet format in a special buffer in the repeater (Figure 4.11a). When there is a gap in the information stream being relayed by the repeater, the ring circuit is broken by the repeater. The buffer is now put into the ring and the information it contains is transmitted to the next node. Since it is impossible for the repeater to stop the other repeater which is upstream of it from continuing to send data, the broken end of the ring is switched into the other end of the buffer and the information read into it as the packet originating at the node is read out (Figure 4.11b). The buffer remains in the ring until the packet which that node sent returns (Figure 4.11c). At that point the buffer is then removed from the circuit (Figure 4.11d).

The diagrams show the technique in only an idealised form. In real implementations extra registers and packet detectors will be used because of the high switching speeds required.

In effect the length of a ring which uses the register insertion method increases as each node places its packet on the ring since the ring circuit is diverted through the buffer. This is the way that the capacity of the ring is increased to accommodate the increasing load. As the number of buffers in the ring increases, the time to transport information around the ring also increases and hence the delay in moving a packet from one location to another. The size of the packets which can be transmitted economically on a register insertion ring is limited by the size of the buffers which can be made which will operate in the manner required. If the buffers are made excessively long, the speed of access to them may be too high and the total transmission time when a large number are in the ring may also be too long, making it more difficult to devise algorithms which will detect lost packets and other error conditions.

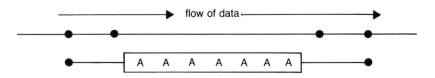

a) Waiting to insert the data

b) Transmitting

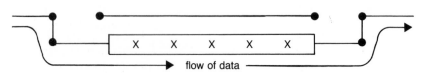

c) Waiting for return of packet

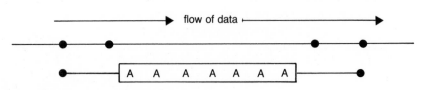

d) Removal of original packet

Figure 4.11   Register Insertion

Token Passing

Although some, if not all, rings are sometimes referred to as token passing schemes, there is one special technique for which the term 'token passing' is reserved. This is the method which uses a specific field or packet which has a unique format and serves only to pass control from one node to another. In empty slot rings the control is passed implicitly when a node repeater has possession of an unused packet. If that node does not want to use it, the packet is passed on to the next repeater in the ring. If the node has information ready to send, it claims the packet for itself and retains it until it is returned. The only token which can be thought of for a register insertion ring is the end of a stream of information at which point the repeater is able to insert the packet which it has ready to send in its buffer.

In a true token passing ring, the special field or packet called the token is circulated around the ring all the time and any node which has a packet ready to send waits until the token is passed to it by the previous node in the ring. When it gets the token, it removes it temporarily from the circuit and starts to transmit its data to the ring (Figure 4.12).

On completion of the transmission of the information, or after it has spent the time allowed when the system was set up, the node places the token at the end of the data and transmits it. The data received by the next node in the ring consists then of a packet or packets of information which originated at the previous node followed immediately by a token (Figure 4.12c). If that node also wishes to send some data, it must relay the packets of information, even if they are addressed to itself, in which case it reads them into its input buffer for subsequent processing, and only when the token arrives can the node remove it temporarily from the circuit and insert its own data as described for the previous node. The resulting situation after two nodes have transmitted information is shown in the figure where two packets of data are being passed around the ring followed by the token.

The string of data continues on its way in this manner with nodes with data to transmit adding their packets of information as they get hold of the token. When a packet reaches its destination, it is normally flagged as having been received by the repeater before being relayed so that the transmitting node knows that the destination has received it.

When the packet is eventually returned to its origin that node removes it from the string of packets. If everything is working as it should then the

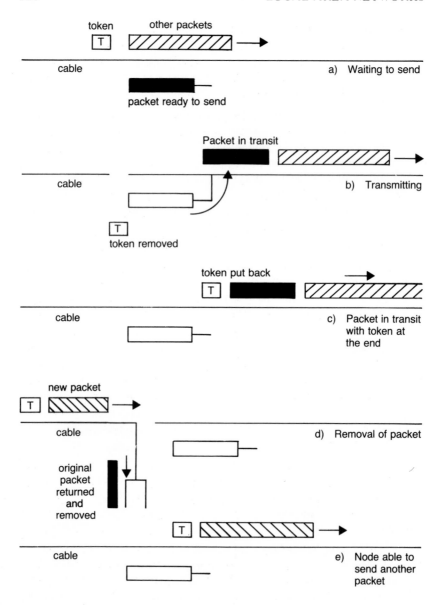

Figure 4.12   Token Passing

packet it sent out last will be the first one in the string which is passed to it, as shown in the figure. However, if a node or its repeater has failed in between sending out the packet and receiving it back again then the packet will not be removed and will circulate indefinitely unless removed by another node such as a monitor station.

The major problem with the token passing method is that tokens themselves may get lost or corrupted and hence become unrecognisable. If a monitor station exists on the ring then one of its jobs would be to always look at the data stream passing by and check that the token is on the end. If it is missing, the monitor would add another. It would also check for more than the specified number of tokens and remove super-fluous ones. If there is no monitor station, although this is unusual for true rings, it would be the task of one or all of the nodes on the ring to generate a new token if the one at the end of the circulating data stream is missing.

If there is no information being passed when the token disappears, the monitor or the other nodes will have a time-out mechanism so that they can generate a new token if none has been passed to them during the set interval. With a monitor station to take charge of this, there is no real problem, but without one it is possible that more than one node will generate tokens at around the same time and so more than one token will exist on the ring. Node repeaters are generally configured to remove extra tokens if they can detect them. They would do this normally by transmitting a packet and then receiving another token before the packet they have just sent out is returned to them. The chance of more than one node generating a token at the same time is minimised by the adoption of a random time-out delay.

Token passing is claimed to make very efficient use of the available capacity of the network. It is adaptable to broadcast bus media as well as sequential configurations such as the ring, although the exact way the two operate is slightly different due to the requirement of the broadcast medium to specifically address each packet and the token itself. How-ever, in the broadcast bus case the information packets are sent direct to the destination even though the control may be sent to another node. The nodes in a ring pass the packets of information from one to another as well as the token. Token passing for broadcast buses is considered separately in an earlier section.

CONCLUSIONS

In this chapter and the previous one, it has been shown that to achieve the design aims of a local area network many different strategies and technologies have been employed. Even using one particular topology and transmission medium, several techniques for operating it have been tried, many with a large measure of success.

Without doubt, no single technique is wholly suitable for every case: the limited bandwidth of some techniques is useless for users who want to use the network for video conferencing, for example, but wide bandwidth networks are more expensive to install and maintain.

To the end-user of the network it is the quality of the service provided which matters, not the technology which is used to transmit the information. At present most local area networks do not insulate the user from the way the network operates although this will probably come in the near future.

To meet the different requirements, several products have been developed and are coming onto the market. Which of these will dominate the market in the end will depend as much on marketing pressures and standards as on their technical merits. The next two chapters will be devoted to examining the research systems and products that have been put together using the materials and techniques described in this and the previous chapter.

5 Research Systems

INTRODUCTION

In the last chapter we examined the techniques which can be used to produce local area networks. It was the bringing together of separate developments which led to the rapid development of the products which are now becoming available. A few research organisations were largely responsible for the systems which have since been adopted by numerous suppliers of computers and communications equipment as the bases for their products. In this chapter we examine selected research systems; in the next we see how they have influenced the development of the resulting products.

During the last few years, several local area networks have been set up in universities and research laboratories to help with interconnecting equipment and to provide a test vehicle for high-speed data transmission techniques over limited distances. Three research systems have probably influenced the development of today's local area networks more than others, namely:

(1) *Ethernet* – a high-speed contention bus network used for digital data transmission over limited distances.

(2) *Cambridge Ring* – the technique of using a continuous loop of cable which operates at high transmission speed to interconnect all devices attached to it.

(3) *MITRENET* – an extension of cable television techniques to data transmission over a small to medium-sized area with extension to voice and visual information easily possible.

ETHERNET

The original Ethernet system was installed on an experimental basis in the Palo Alto Research Center of the Xerox Corporation in California during the early 1970s. Its purpose was to connect office workstations to expensive computing resources or other office machinery so that they could be shared by everybody with a workstation.

The main design objectives were:

— to design a communications system for an office environment which had the potential to grow smoothly with increasing demand;

— to accommodate several buildings containing personal workstations, computers and other computing facilities;

— to provide a communications network that would be cheap to install and run, since the workstations were to be fairly cheap;

— to provide a reliable network;

— to concentrate control of the network in one location or device;

— to achieve very low overheads in maintaining and running the system;

— to provide a network that would be suited to handling data traffic in bursts.

It was decided that reliability and cheapness could best be achieved by making the network as simple as possible. The requirement to handle bursty traffic meant that normal techniques for polling and time division multiplexing would not be the answer. It was decided, therefore, to adopt the University of Hawaii's approach used in their ALOHA network of distributing control of the network to every user, but adapting the technique to minimise wasted transmission time caused by two or more users sending at the same instant.

The medium chosen for the network was coaxial cable because it was easy to obtain and connect devices to, was capable of carrying high-speed transmissions and was comparatively cheap.

The topology used for Ethernet was an unrooted tree in which only one path must exist between any two points; otherwise, packets would reach the destination by several routes and consequently be out of synchronisation due to different path lengths.

The key to Ethernet is not the medium nor the topology, but it is the way the medium is used. The medium is shared by all the users and each may transmit packets of information at any time. Each packet contains a header which specifies the address of the destination but every other user listens to every packet transmission. The sender relies on the intended recipient hearing the transmission and reading it into its own store for subsequent processing. The other users of the network should ignore the transmissions which are not addressed to them, nor should they transmit whilst someone else is using the network. There is no automatic acknowledgement that the packet has been successfully received built into the technique. Higher levels of protocol are needed to send back explicit acknowledgement packets, or requests for retransmission if an error in the packet was detected by the recipient.

Ethernet uses a development of the Carrier Sense Multiple Access technique (CSMA). The designers recognised that packets in transit on the network are very likely to overlap with one another and therefore they made specific provision in the design to handle collisions.

For the reasons explained in the chapter on Network Sharing Techniques (Chapter 4), the designers of Ethernet developed the variant of CSMA now called CSMA/CD (Carrier Sense Multiple Access with Collision Detection). By doing so, the amount of time wasted whilst packets collide was minimised. The full details of the original Ethernet design are given in reference 5.1.

The capacity of the Ethernet network is fairly divided amongst the users only if all of them abide by the same rules. Stations can take unfair advantage of the technique by various means: eg not waiting before attempting retransmission after a collision has occurred; not adjusting the interval after two successive collisions; and sending large packets. The responsibility for fair use of the network lies with every device using it.

The Ethernet technique has been the subject of many investigations in an effort to make it fairer, but in practice the system has worked well. The criticisms normally levelled against it are:

—   no upper bound on the maximum number of collisions which can occur;

—   collided packets are discriminated against by delaying them; this means that devices which experience several successive collisions are made to wait for an unreasonable length of time;

— there is a wide variation of waiting times.

The most favoured techniques for reducing these inefficiencies are so-called 'slotted' Ethernet schemes. Here the CSMA/CD technique is normally used, but after collisions occur, the channel is allocated to different users on a slotted basis, so avoiding another collision with the same packet. The HYPERchannel scheme, described in the next chapter, is an example of this technique.

The Ethernet Installation

The experimental system installed at the Palo Alto Research Center of Xerox had the following features:

— length 1 km, based on the attenuation in the medium and the need for easy design of the transmitting and receiving devices;

— speed 3 Mbps, which was suited to the minicomputers used on the network and reduced the need for special buffers between internal storage and the communications system;

— maximum number of stations (ie transmitting and receiving devices directly attached to the network) was 256. This was limited by the tapping techniques used and was to give a reasonable level of access by the users;

— the medium used was low-loss off-the-shelf coaxial cable with standard cable television taps and connectors;

— transceivers used limited power baseband transmission with isolation circuits so that they could not pollute the medium if they failed to work correctly;

— bit serial transmission of packets;

— a controller was needed for every station to implement the protocol for sending and receiving packets.

The original Ethernet concept proved so successful for office communications that several experimental systems were installed by adventurous organisations as well as in several Xerox office locations. The basic techniques employed have been carried forward into the design of an uprated Ethernet (called Ethernet II) which uses longer packets, better addressing and a higher transmission speed (reference 5.2). The CSMA/CD protocol has remained essentially the same, indicating that it has worked well.

CAMBRIDGE RING

During 1974 Professor Wilkes of the University of Cambridge visited the laboratories of the Swiss telecommunication company Hasler, where he saw an experimental ring-shaped system being developed for carrying digitised speech. Since the information carried on the network was in digital form, Professor Wilkes saw that it had the potential to be developed for interconnecting computer equipment.

At that time the University of Cambridge Computer Laboratory had the need to interconnect computers and similar devices within a building in a network which was capable of operating at a data rate substantially greater than that provided by conventional communications techniques. The network, as well as needing to be very high speed, simple to design and implement, had to be able to prevent a single device from hogging all the network capacity.

The Hasler ring used the register insertion technique for transmitting information round the ring at 10 Mbps. The Cambridge people considered this transmission rate to be more than adequate for their needs so their adaptation of the design did not make any effort to ensure an efficient use of the available bandwidth.

The first experimental ring at Cambridge used the register insertion technique and established that the concept was feasible. However, there was some concern expressed regarding the maintenance and reliability problems in running a register insertion ring. Briefly, when a node on the ring sends a packet, it switches into the ring a register or buffer which contains the packet and this stays in series with the ring until removed by the return of the packet or by some other means. The register in fact lengthens the ring for the period when it is in the circuit. If the register switching circuits have an error and cannot be switched out of the ring then the performance of the whole ring is degraded. The switching circuitry must also be fast enough to add the register to the ring and remove it without the loss of any digits and without upsetting the modulation technique. For these, and other reasons, the Cambridge team decided that a better solution to their problems was to use another scheme for transporting information based on a continuously circulating packet – the *empty slot* technique (reference 5.3).

The empty slot technique for rings has been fully described in an earlier chapter. The Cambridge installation uses the technique in a reasonably standard form with the addition of a monitoring station to help maintain

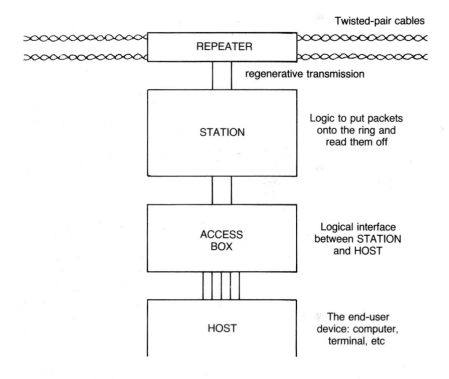

Figure 5.1   Cambridge Ring Hardware for Each Interface

ring integrity, although this is not strictly necessary for the technique to work.

The ring at Cambridge was originally short and only one slot was used. Now the ring is over 1 km long and has 36 nodes (or stations) attached with 4 slots circulating at 10 Mbps.

A baseband signalling system is used with two pairs of twisted-pair cable. The cable is the type normally employed for duplex operation of teletypes. The way the data is encoded on the wires is as follows: a change of state on both pairs simultaneously is used to indicate a bit value of 1; a change on one pair only indicates a bit value of 0. In the latter case each pair is used alternately.

The way the ring is tapped at each node is shown in Figure 5.1. The *repeater* is attached directly to the wires which make up the ring. Its purpose is to regenerate the input signals, transmit them to the next node and make them available for reading by the attached devices, data flow round the ring being in one direction only. Since they are active components, the repeaters are generally powered directly from the ring with a DC voltage being provided by the pairs of cables used for data transmission. This is one of the ways that ring integrity is ensured since then the repeaters can continue to operate without the device which is attached to them needing to be working, or even plugged in. The repeater operates very rapidly and imposes very little delay on the data travelling round the ring.

Attached to the repeater is a device called the *station*. This contains the logic needed to put packets onto the ring and read them off. Because the empty slot technique is used, the station with a packet to send must first wait for an empty slot to reach the repeater. This is recognised as soon as the second bit in the slot is received. The repeater sets the full/empty bit to 'full' and the station fills up the data fields as the slot is passing through the repeater. No extra delay is imposed on the slot, nor does the apparent length of the ring alter as would happen with a register insertion ring. The station can be set to reject or accept all the packets, or just accept those addressed specifically to it.

Attached to the station is the *Access Box* which provides the logical interface between the station and the host device (ie the computer, terminal or peripheral controller). The access box has to perform the buffering, flow control and other functions expected by the host device.

The format of the slot is shown in Figure 5.2. The first bit indicates the start of a slot. The next bit says whether the slot is being used or not, and the third bit is used by the monitor to check the operation of the ring. Taken together, bits 2 and 3 are used as follows:

11 — set by transmitter. Indicates 'full' and 'monitor not passed'.

10 — set by monitor as slot passes it. Indicates 'full' and 'monitor passed once'.

00 — set by transmitter when the slot returns. Indicates 'empty slot'.

01 — set by the monitor in an empty slot. The monitor sets zero or random bits in the data field and, if on return bits 2 and 3 are still 01, it checks that the data is still set correctly.

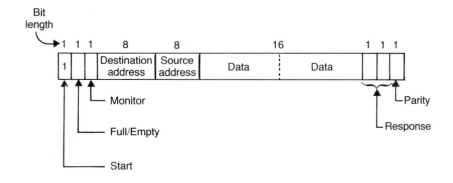

Figure 5.2   Cambridge Ring Packet Format

10 — detected by the monitor. If it receives a slot with 10 set in bits 2 and 3, it indicates that a full slot has not been removed by the transmitter after passing once round the loop. The monitor resets the slot to 'empty' and logs the error.

The next 8 bits are used to indicate the address of the destination. Certain special addresses are reserved: address 0 is the monitor station and is used by stations reporting errors; address 255 is a broadcast packet and is intended for every station on the network.

The next 8 bits are used for the address of the sender, and these are followed by two bytes of data.

The response bits following the data field are set as follows:

11 — set by transmitter. If they are still set on return the transmitter knows the data was *ignored*.

10 — set by the receiver to tell the transmitter the packet has been *rejected*.

01 — set by the receiver to indicate that the packet was *accepted*.

00 — set by the receiver to tell the transmitter that it was *busy* and unable to process the packet.

The last bit is the parity bit. This is checked by every repeater, and reset correctly by each one. If a repeater gets a packet which has a parity error, it sends a reporting packet to the Monitor station in the first empty packet it can obtain. Thus the Monitor can detect where a packet in error is detected and can report faults to the network supervisor.

A continuous stream of zeros being received by any station indicates that no packets (full or empty) are in transit. This could indicate a break in the ring and can be used to report errors.

The key to the successful operation of the Cambridge ring is the quality of the repeater. With a system based on twisted-pair cables, the repeaters must not be too far apart, not because of signal attenuation as is often supposed, but because the signalling system uses four wires and any small percentage difference in length will cause slight differences in propagation times between repeaters, causing the signals to become out of phase. By very carefully matching the cables used, greater distances between repeaters can be accepted, but this is not generally worth the trouble and cost.

The original repeaters at Cambridge were hand-made in the laboratory but later printed circuits were available which made the manufacture of the repeaters quicker and more reliable. The latest development is to incorporate most of the discrete components in a special LSI chip made from Ferranti's Uncommitted Logic Array (ULA) chips. Two different ones are being used: one for the repeater itself and one for the station.

As a result of experience gained in using the ring at Cambridge and elsewhere, the opportunity was taken to alter the format of the slot during the design of the ULA chips. After some experiments it was decided to add 2 extra control bits, make the data field variable length from 1 to 8 bytes, use more elaborate maintenance packets, and provide an option for a station to retain the use of a slot instead of flagging it empty and passing it on after one revolution of the ring.

The production of reliable ULA chips has taken much longer than was originally intended so a number of companies started marketing devices (mainly repeaters, stations and some access boxes) for the Cambridge Ring made up from discrete components. Although these products all use the same empty slot technique, different methods have been adopted for wiring the repeaters together, different voltages have been employed for the repeaters, different slot formats are sometimes used, and different techniques for attaching the host systems. This can give problems to installations with devices from more than one manufacturer.

In practice the Cambridge Ring has the following characteristics. Although the basic transmission rate is 10 Mbps, a station cannot transmit at this rate since it cannot use every slot and must wait for each packet to return and then empty the slot. It also has to inspect the response bits of the returned packet before deciding its next action. At best, in a ring with n circulating slots, each station can transmit only once per (n + 2) slots. As ring size increases, so the number of circulating slots may increase, so reducing the point-to-point bandwidth. Increasing the basic data rate does not improve the point-to-point performance since the number of packets in use will increase, but the total system bandwidth improves. For a typical ring operating at 10 Mbps with 2 circulating slots, the maximum transmission rate of a station is slightly over 1 Mbps, excluding overheads.

Having said this, the ring has proved very reliable in operation, with an extremely low error rate in spite of the simple error detection system used. The fact that the ring does not allow one station to hog the ring capacity means that under heavy loads it performs well and each node is given a fair share of the bandwidth.

By changing components in the repeaters it is possible to increase the speed easily to 20 Mbps and experiments have been conducted on a 100 Mbps ring using bigger slots and different components.

Another possibility which has been considered is the use of different length slots circulating at the same time; for example, a 2 slot ring with one slot containing one byte of data and the other slot with 8 bytes of data. By using the slot retention option referred to earlier (ie a station not releasing the slot after one revolution) on the larger slot only, the ring can be used for rapid transfer of large quantities of data without preventing everybody else from using the ring.

An experiment to use the ring to transfer digitised voice traffic has been carried out and has demonstrated its feasibility. It is estimated that a normal 10 Mbps ring could carry 64 simultaneous telephone conversations provided it was not needed for data as well.

The Cambridge Computer Laboratory, and other universities which have been involved, have designed a set of higher level protocols for use with the Cambridge Ring. The basic empty slot protocol is just a bit moving procedure and requires a higher level to allow whole packets of data (in the way normally understood by computer programmers and users) to be transmitted and error checked, etc. The access boxes at the nodes on the ring can also be made to serve more than one end-user host or terminal provided that a protocol is used which can distinguish port or logical addresses of the packets of data carried across the network.

To these ends, the following protocols are used at Cambridge.

Basic Block Protocol

A basic block is a datagram or packet (not to be confused with the packet which fits in a slot for transport round the ring). Its format is shown in Figure 5.3. The port number is the address of the application program or separate devices served by that ring station. This enables a single device, such as a host computer, to be in conversation with several other devices at the same time. The access box or host system uses these port numbers to direct the incoming blocks of data.

Single Shot Protocol

The idea behind the Single Shot Protocol is to serve simple transactions which consist of a single basic block request which requires only a single basic block reply. The request block is identified by a special bit pattern in the header and it can contain function and parameter fields. The reply can include a return code indicating the success or failure of the request and various parameters as well as data.

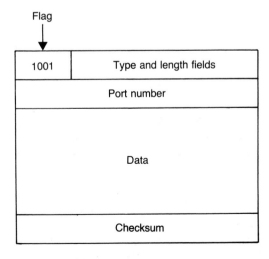

Figure 5.3   Cambridge Ring Basic Block

Byte Stream Protocol

To handle the transfer of long messages, files or character streams, a further level of protocol is required since a single basic block cannot contain sufficient data for the transfer to be carried out with the single shot protocol. This is the function of the Byte Stream Protocol. In effect the Byte Stream Protocol uses a series of basic blocks to set up a virtual circuit between the sending application or device and the receiver. It then transfers the stream of characters and then closes down the virtual circuit.

Most of the implementations of the Cambridge Ring provide all of the above three protocols since they are the basis for any user communications programming.

MITRENET

The Mitre Corporation in the USA has made considerable efforts to develop a local area networking system which gives it room for expansion (reference 5.4). The reasons behind its efforts were the growing number of users of Mitre's host computer systems and the wide range of applications being developed. During the 1970s, as the number of users increased, so did the number of terminals and host processors. Users did not want to be constrained to using just one host from their terminal and the thought of a separate terminal for each host, together with all the extra cabling required, was the spur to developing an integrated communications system, and more recently a multifunction terminal.

The Mitre computer systems provided users with the normal data processing facilities, word-processing, electronic mail and software development. The word-processing facilities were provided by one host and the electronic mail by another.

The Mitre Corporation decided to apply the hardware techniques from the cable television industry (CATV) to the problems of data transmission. One of the most appealing features of the CATV technology was the enormous bandwidth (300-400 MHz) available with standard equipment. With such a wide bandwidth very great quantities of data could be transmitted at high speeds.

One of the problems with using wide-band modulated transmissions for data had been the inefficient use of the available bandwidth. Take, for example, a channel 300 MHz wide and divide it up into a series of bands, each wide enough to carry data at the required rate. Thus a data transmission rate of 64 kbps may require a bandwidth of 150 kHz, depending on the modulation technique, overheads and separation from adjacent bands required. Two of these channels would be required to provide a send and receive channel making a total of 300 kHz per channel or pair of devices. Thus, 1000 such channels could be accommodated within the total system bandwidth but in normal circumstances each of these would be severely under-used. There is also the problem of switching from one frequency band to another when they require to send to another device.

Mitre decided that the CATV technology could, with advantage, be combined with time division multiple access techniques to offer a near-perfect solution to local digital communications. Such a technique could provide:

—   high data transmission speeds;

—   high bandwidth available allowing minimum waiting time before transmitting;

—   distances between devices not limited to one or two kilometres.

The first major system that Mitre developed was known as MITRIX. Briefly it used simple time division multiplexing to allow each user to access the network:

—   time slots were assigned to each user;

—   each user was allocated the number of slots in relation to the data rate at which they expected to transmit: eg 300 bps terminals would get 4 slots in same time interval; 9.6 kbps devices would get 128 slots in the same interval;

—   the aggregate data transmission rate was 819.2 kbps.

The MITRIX system proved to be good for the users who transmitted data fairly continuously, but poor when a large number of users demanded connection simultaneously. There were too many slow speed devices using the network so the overall use of the network was inefficient. Also the demand for use of the network grew more quickly than expected.

The network was subsequently developed into a *dual-mode* system, MITRIX II, using a slotted ALOHA multiple access technique. The dual-mode referred to the fact that high usage devices were assigned dedicated unique slots, but low speed or bursty devices could share a common set of slots. This system required that the devices sharing slots had to examine the messages for collisions, and back-off if one occurred. The system aggregate rate was much higher than MITRIX, around 7.4 Mbps, and overall it was reasonably efficient and supported all types of device well.

Mitre's third development was MITRENET, during the late 1970s. This is a contention bus scheme using CATV technology. A similar scheme for accessing and using the bus to that employed by Ethernet is used; namely CSMA/CD. Because CATV uses broadband Radio Frequency transmissions and a different data transmission speed from Ethernet, a different collision detection technique must be employed. CSMA/CD allows the bus to transmit variable length packets instead of those determined by the time slot size used in the earlier schemes. It is efficient for all classes of user, as are most CSMA/CD systems.

Thus Mitre have developed a broadband contention bus system which is essentially the same in operation as the baseband Ethernet network. But broadband networks are capable of considerable expansion since a single bus with a capacity of 10 Mbps (the same as Ethernet II) does not use up very much of the 300-400 kHz bandwidth which is available.

MITRENET can use the whole of the 300 MHz channel it has allocated for data transmission and another 300 kHz wide channel for receiving by employing two cables instead of one (see Figure 5.4). It was argued that

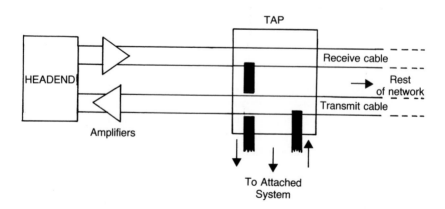

Figure 5.4   Mitre Two-Cable System and the Tap

since the installation cost of the cable ducts is very much higher than the cable which goes in them, then two cables per duct may just as well be installed with the added advantage that the available bandwidth would then be double. Transmission is always along one cable which the headend device receives and retransmits down the receive cable.

Mitre are experimenting with network control and monitoring of the network using a minicomputer which listens to the transmission. Continuity testing (by means of loopback systems) is also being introduced.

Since the CATV system was designed for analogue transmission, television in particular, it is no real problem to allocate channels for voice and video as well as data. This is the advantage of CATV systems. Against this must be off-set the extra cost of providing RF modems to modulate the data onto the appropriate carrier frequency. These are generally more expensive than the simpler baseband network interfaces used by some other systems.

6 Recent Developments

INTRODUCTION

During 1981 new local area network products were being announced at such a high rate that it was a full-time task keeping up with them. Not only were well-known computer suppliers involved but also companies which had been newly formed to market these systems, or which were new to the UK. Well established companies in the data communications field were also looking to widen their product range by introducing local area networks with the promise that a gateway to the public networks, such as PSS in the UK, would be available in the near future. This indicates that it is expected that users will soon see the need to interconnect their local area networks which could well be situated in different locations.

In view of the number of products on the market, and the way the situation is changing so rapidly, it is unrealistic here to attempt to survey the marketplace. What can be done, however, is to examine the main trends and see how these are building on the earlier experimental systems.

TYPES OF TECHNIQUES

We can classify the techniques into the following broad types:

Baseband Contention Bus Systems

These are systems which are often referred to as 'Ethernet-type' although in practice a different method of accessing the bus can be, and often is, used. The common feature is a baseband signalling system over a single physical channel which is shared with everyone.

139

Cambridge Ring Types

By Cambridge Ring types are meant ring-shaped networks which operate on the circulating empty slot principle. Most of this type of ring on the market at present are modelled very closely on the Cambridge Ring implemented at the Cambridge Computer Laboratory.

Broadband Networks

A category of network which is rapidly rising in importance is the broadband system which uses modulated carrier signals and frequency division techniques to allocate several separate channels on one or two cables. Each channel may be used in different ways.

Register Insertion Rings

Register insertion techniques for transmission on rings have been around for some time but few products using the technique exist. However, one supplier is developing a local area network which promises to have a significant market.

Token Access Systems

Although few network products are currently available which use a proper token access technique, the fact that it is a fair and efficient technique, and a candidate for standardisation in the USA, means that it is likely to be important in the future.

Other Systems

A few other systems are under development which cannot conveniently be classified in one of the above categories.

BASEBAND CONTENTION BUS SYSTEMS

Ethernet-Based Systems

The outstanding success of Ethernet as an experimental system has given rise to a lot of interest in local area networks. Some organisations who could not wait for official products installed the experimental version of Ethernet used at Xerox's Palo Alto Research Center (PARC) so that they could evaluate it in their own environment. Independent computer and communications systems suppliers have also gone ahead and developed their versions of CSMA/CD systems differing in such things as transmission speed and packet format from both of the two Ethernet systems which have been published.

One of the reasons for the interest in Ethernet is the fact that it has been shown to be efficient in use within the office environment, and it is just this market where the major computing developments are likely to come in the next decade. Monitoring the Xerox PARC network in 1979 showed that most Ethernet packets were very small (80% were less than 30 bytes in length) and that the peak utilisation of the network was not high, and well within the capacity of the system in spite of its low speed when compared with the latest developments.

A significant development in Ethernet was the agreement in 1980 between Digital Equipment Corporation, Intel Corporation and Xerox Corporation to jointly develop Ethernet as an industry standard local area network. To meet this requirement this consortium have published the document *The Ethernet. A Local Area Network. Data Link Layer and Physical Layer Specifications* (reference 6.1). This document contains a full description of the physical data transmission and further documents describe the addressing conventions and higher level protocols. In summary the Ethernet specified by this document is as follows:

Medium: shielded coaxial cable of high quality with a solid central conductor and a braided shield. The jacket should be marked with annular rings at 2.5 metre intervals to assist in the correct placement of the transceivers. Incorrect spacing causes RF interference problems. The characteristic impedance of the cable must be 50 ohms and all connectors should have the same impedance. Terminators of 50 ohms impedance must also be fixed to prevent reflections.

Signalling technique: baseband Manchester encoding

Maximum station separation: 2.5 km

Maximum length of a cable segment: 500 metres

Maximum number of stations: 1024

Data transmission rate: 10 Mbps

Access method: CSMA/CD. The Ethernet implementation of this access technique is the standard one with no priority scheme built into it. If there is a collision between packets, the transmitting stations involved back off for a random length of time and then attempt to transmit again. If they again experience a collision, they back off for longer. If after 16 attempts, the transmission of that packet has still not succeeded then the attempt is abandoned and the station reports a possible station or network failure.

Frame: The format of an Ethernet frame is shown in Figure 6.1. Its length, including the Preamble field, can vary from 72 to 1526 bytes. The Data portion of the frame occupies 46 to 1500 bytes. The Preamble is a special sequence of characters, represented in binary by 10 10 10 10 repeated 7 times followed by 10 10 10 11, which is needed to ensure that the electronic circuits in the transceivers reach a steady state and lock on to the signal timing before the frame proper is transmitted. The last two bits of the preamble are both 1s to indicate its end in case the transceivers

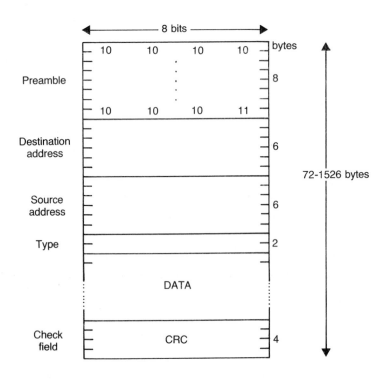

Figure 6.1   Ethernet Packet Format

missed the true start. The next bit transmitted is the start of the Destination address field.

Addressing: The address fields may, at first sight, appear to be unnecessarily long since only 1024 stations per network are permitted. The 48 bits of the addresses permit over 280 million million different values. The Xerox view is that Ethernet local area networks are only one part of a full set of networks which they call *Internetwork* systems. The address numbering scheme should be capable of handling this global set of networks. It is intended that:

— devices should be uniquely addressable by high-level software;

— groups of devices should be addressable;

— the system should have potential for growth.

The 48 bit address field is divided into three sections as shown in Figure 6.2. Twenty-three bits are used as block numbers, the intention being that each user or manufacturer uses a single or small number of blocks for their Ethernet devices. This number allows 2^{23} (= 8,388,608) blocks to be assigned. Within each block there are another 2^{24} (= 16,777,216) numbers which can be allocated to individual devices. When a block owner has used all the numbers in one block he may then ask for another block to be assigned to him. In this manner every Ethernet device or Ethernet interface chip should have a unique address. Block numbers are assigned by Xerox, device numbers by the owner of the block. The

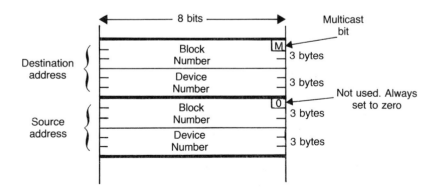

Figure 6.2 Ethernet Address Field Format

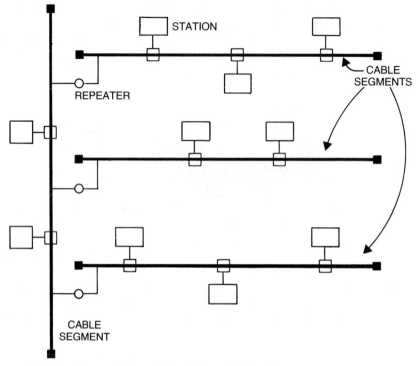

Figure 6.3   Ethernet Topology

remaining bit in the destination field is the *Multicast* bit. This is set to 1 by the transmitter if every device within a group or block is to receive the transmission. The corresponding bit in the source address field is not used.

Network Topology: Ethernet networks can be branching non-rooted tree shaped, with no more than two repeater stations between any two devices. In practice this means that the network will have the shape shown in Figure 6.3. No two transceivers on the system may be separated by more than 1500 metres.

It costs $1000 to get a licence to develop Ethernet products. This is obtained from Xerox who then will provide all the necessary literature and allocate block numbers. A large number of suppliers have now obtained licences.

A small British Company, Sension Scientific Ltd, have developed a special transceiver which is inserted into the cable rather than being tapped into it as is the usual Ethernet installation. This requires the coaxial cable to be cut but it is said to eliminate the need to tap in only at the special intervals marked by the rings on the cable. Even when the transceiver is not in use its presence does not prevent the whole of the Ethernet cable from being used by other stations.

To Xerox, Ethernet is only the backbone communications network for their range of office products, which in turn were developed from their research systems. Xerox now provide a range of devices which are specifically designed to be interconnected using Ethernet. Devices from other manufacturers require extra equipment in order to use Ethernet. The two approaches are shown in Figure 6.4. The controller can be either a separate device which provides interfaces specifically for the attached device (eg RS-232C) or it can be incorporated in the device itself. The Xerox 8010 workstation (known as the Star Information System) is one of the products designed for use with Ethernet. It consists of a processor, display, disk files and various other features and is intended for use as a workstation in a network which may contain, in addition to other similar workstations, a shared filing system, printers, communications devices, etc.

The Ungermann-Bass organisation of California have adopted the other approach to Ethernet and they supply the basic communications network on to which users can attach their own terminals and processors.

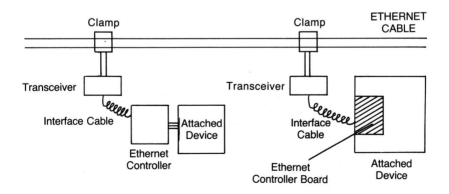

Figure 6.4   Methods of Attaching to Ethernet

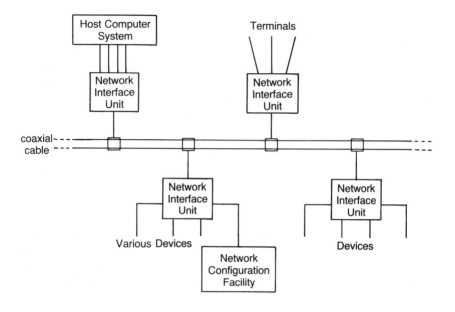

Figure 6.5   Net/One Configuration

This company was one of the first to provide an Ethernet system, called Net/One, although the early version was not to the full Ethernet specification. That network operated at 4 Mbps. When the full Ethernet specification was published by DEC, Intel and Xerox, Ungermann-Bass updated their Net/One to run at 10 Mbps and follow all the other requirements of Ethernet.

Net/One is shown diagrammatically in Figure 6.5. It consists of the standard Ethernet coaxial cable to which the Ethernet controllers, called Network Interface Units (NIUs), are attached via simple transceivers and cable taps. The NIUs are each capable of supporting a number of end-user devices (up to 24 per NIU) via their normal interfaces. The NIUs each contain several microprocessors and memory and are loaded, when they are switched on, with software from the Network Configuration Facility, which itself is attached to an NIU and has back-up storage and a console through which the network supervisor can configure the network and monitor its use.

In Net/One the basic Ethernet transmission system has been extended with interface software and hardware for a range of user devices, and a facility to establish virtual circuits between these devices on the network. These virtual circuits can be created either by the user, by means of commands to the network software, or by the network supervisor. If a particular device always needs to interact with another on the network then the NIU can be configured to set up a virtual circuit between these two devices whenever the system is turned on. The network supervisor can also set up and destroy virtual circuits.

Because the users interact only through their Network Interface Units it is possible to alter the physical medium which is used. Ungermann-Bass are currently experimenting with a broadband-based transmission system running at around 5 Mbps but still using the standard Ethernet CSMA/CD access mechanism. Their argument is that baseband transmission using standard Ethernet cable is not always the best solution for every situation. Some environments and modes of use are better served by the broadband CATV method of transmission. By altering the NIUs, different physical media can be accommodated without altering the way the user interacts with the system.

Onto the Net/One set of facilities another level can be built and this is what the UK supplier of communications equipment, CASE, has decided to do. CASE decided to enhance their range of communications equipment and extend their market to the office environment by introducing a local area network into their product range. This they call CASENET and it uses Net/One as the basic communications system to which are added software and interfaces to some of their message switching systems and multiplexers. Using their DCX range of multiplexers, CASE can provide a range of gateways between Ethernet networks, and between Ethernet and public data networks, telex, teletex, etc.

Voice Traffic

Ethernet is primarily a data carrying network but many users would like to see their data and telephone traffic carried on a single network within the confines of a single site or office block. If this could be achieved, the amount of cabling needed could be reduced, at the same time allowing for the better integration of voice and data in the electronic office. A substantial amount of work has been done in recent years on the digitising of voice and its transport in packets. This is not the place to discuss all the experiments, problems and successes of this work but we will discuss the work which the Xerox Corporation and others have done using Ethernet.

To carry voice traffic through a packet network requires that the analogue signals are first digitised. This is done by sampling the voice signal and producing digital signals at regular intervals. The most common system used is *Pulse Code Modulation* (PCM) in which the system samples the analogue waveform at 8 kHz, producing an 8-bit value for each sample. This requires a total digital data rate for each voice signal of 64 kbps. This is a very high bandwidth and the resulting voice quality, when it is converted back to the analogue form, is very good. Experiments have been done with alternative coding and sampling schemes and it is possible to reduce the digital data rate down to 16 kbps whilst retaining adequate voice quality. One other way of reducing the continuous data rate that needs to be supported is to detect and not transmit silent passages.

Using the minimum data rate possible is essential when one comes to employ a contention bus such as Ethernet to transmit voice traffic. Some of the most disconcerting aspects of telephone conversations to the users are the gaps between words, when the listener does not know whether the speaker has stopped talking or whether there has been a break in the circuit. The 'high-level protocols' with which human beings converse with one another, especially over the telephone, use pauses to indicate many things, including the cessation of a passage of speech but sometimes also to emphasise something. Normal telephone circuits transmit the analogue waveforms in more or less real time but contention bus digital systems have to split up the speech into packets and transmit each one separately. If there are considerable delays between packets, due perhaps to the network being busy and the sender not being able to transmit immediately, the reconstructed speech at the other end will be fragmented. Transmitting 64 kbps continuously over a period will use up a very considerable portion of the Ethernet bandwidth of 10 Mbps absolute maximum. This is only for one side of the conversation. For a normal full-duplex telephone conversation 128 kbps will be required using the standard PCM techniques. Hence it is important to reduce the data rate required as much as possible and not transmit 'empty' frames when the corresponding partner is not speaking.

However, with the transmission of speech it is far less important that every bit is accurately received. The human beings involved at the ends can usually understand conversations even when they have been severely distorted by the transmission medium. Unfortunately the more sophisticated encoding techniques used to reduce the bandwidth required are less able to handle errors and still reconstruct the original signal in a recognisable form.

Xerox used an experimental Ethernet system for their voice traffic investigations. This ran at 2.94 Mbps, and standard 64 kbps voice digitising. The experiments were very limited and showed that the system behaved well under the loads they placed on it. (For full details see reference 6.2.) Using reasonably efficient encoding methods and silence suppression it was estimated that several hundred users could be accommodated on an Ethernet network. Possibly the most useful application to which the technique could be applied in the short term and in the context of local area networks, is that of a centralised voice storage system, possibly for dictation or message recording. In this manner a fragmented conversation would not matter so much since the digitised conversation would still be stored continuously, and on play-back would not need to be disjointed.

HYPERchannel and HYPERbus

The Network Systems Corporation of the USA have developed and are marketing a contention bus system which differs substantially from Ethernet. Two separate systems using their technique are available and are aimed at different requirements. HYPERchannel is intended for linking together mainframe computer systems, minicomputers, and their peripherals and is capable of supporting very high data transfer rates. HYPERbus is a low-speed version and is more typical of the usual local area network in that it is intended for interconnecting terminals and computer systems.

Each system uses a baseband bit-serial bus to transport the data. The bus is shared by all the users of the network using the CSMA/CA technique described in Chapter 4. To understand how the bus is accessed let us consider the state in which the bus has been idle for some time and a user or device wants to transmit a packet of information The state of the bus over a period of time is shown in Figure 6.6. The device which has a packet to send first listens to the bus, and hearing that it is idle, it transmits immediately. As soon as the transmission ceases, the destination device, assuming no collisions have occurred, sends back an acknowledgement, which is a short packet. It is the network interface device which sends these acknowledgements under hardware control so that there is very little time wasted. The acknowledgement itself cannot collide with any

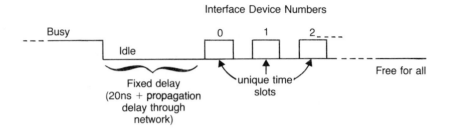

Figure 6.6   HYPERchannel Time Allocation

other packet because after each packet is sent, the network enters a phase where each station has a fixed time slot.

Thus, each time the network is used it enters a state in which each station is allowed to transmit only during a pre-allocated time slot. In this way no collisions are possible except during the 'free-for-all' phase which is entered after the pre-allocated slots have all passed and none has been used. The time slots can be allocated on a priority basis. When the bus is very busy the network remains in the pre-allocated slot state all the time, thus avoiding any collisions. When there is little traffic the network will be in the 'free-for-all' state most of the time. In the latter state it is possible that one transmission will collide with another. When this happens the destination device will either not recognise the packet as being addressed to it or will detect an error. In either case it will not send an acknow- ledgement packet. Since the network was busy during this period when a collision occurs it will then enter the pre-allocated time slot state and so the lost packets can be re-transmitted in the appropriate slot without fear of being lost again.

It is possible that high output devices could get an unfair proportion of the bandwidth if they have a high priority slot. To avoid this happening in practice a delay is imposed by the stations so that after transmitting one packet they cannot send another until they have delayed for long enough to give other users a chance.

HYPERchannel can support up to 4 separate buses, each of which transmits at 50 Mbps. HYPERbus uses a single bus which operates at 6.312 Mbps. Each system uses intelligent interface units which are attached to the cable and which perform the bus access and control as well as interfacing to the end-user devices.

Whilst discussing HYPERchannel mention should be made of MASS-NET. This is a set of software based on HYPERchannel which provides access to applications. (HYPERchannel provides the access to the devices, not the programs within them.) MASSNET provides subroutine interfaces for COBOL, PL/1, FORTRAN, etc, end-to-end protocols, error recovery, etc, for programs to communicate with each other. MASSNET software resides in the host computers and communicates with the HYPERchannel software interfaces.

Microcomputer Networks

Some suppliers of microcomputer systems have realised the potential of connecting together microcomputers and personal workstations using local area networks. Some have opted to use CSMA/CD techniques but have adapted them to the particular requirements of microcomputer systems.

Typical of these is the Cluster/One network designed by NESTAR in the USA and supplied in the UK by Zynar. The Cluster/One system was originally intended to link microcomputers from different manufacturers but soon it was decided to standardise on the Apple II personal computer system. CSMA/CD access techniques are used but it does not really resemble Ethernet in any other respect. The medium for interconnection is multi-way cable, usually 16-wire ribbon cable but round multicore wire can also be used. The transmission speed over the network is 240 kbps and the total cable length supported for each network is 300 metres. Small packets (less than or equal to 256 bytes of data) are used for data transmission, and the number of workstations on the network must not exceed 64.

By using this simplified technique, and by restricting the length of the bus and the speed, NESTAR have been able to provide network interfaces very cheaply, when compared with those built to the full Ethernet specification. For a network composed entirely of Apple microcomputers this restriction is not serious. The signalling system used can be very simple because of the multi-wire bus used. One wire can be used to indicate that the network is in use by one of the stations, the other wires can be used to carry clocking information and the data in parallel form.

The NESTAR system is significant in that it is marketed as an office system with a range of applications and services which are used in the typical office environment: for example, electronic mail, word processing, electronic filing and information handling and in-house viewdata. Wherever possible, the system builds on software which is readily available for the Apple range of personal microcomputers. Most importantly, the network allows all the workstations to share a single high-speed disk store and various printers.

Zynar have indicated that when single-chip Ethernet interfaces are readily and cheaply available, the network may be updated to incorporate these.

The UK microcomputer company Acorn has adopted a similar approach with its *Econet* system. Again the CSMA/CD access technique is used with a data transmission rate of around 210 kbps. The cabling used is dual twisted-pair wire and the cost of providing network access is very low for each microcomputer. A centralised file storage system is provided, which again is similar to the NESTAR system. The major market for Econet appears to be in education since many of the features are ideal for teaching how to use computers. For example, the screen image on one microcomputer can be displayed on all the others, one computer can control the others, and software can be down-line loaded.

The microprocessor and microcomputer company Zilog also have adopted a similar strategy to interconnect their microcomputers with *Z-Net*. Z-Net can accommodate up to 255 stations on a network with a total length of over 4000 feet. One of the devices is usually a high-speed disk system which is shared by all the other users, generally MCZ-2 microcomputers. Z-Net uses a single coaxial cable and CSMA/CD access methods, and the data transfer rate is 800 kbps.

CAMBRIDGE RING TYPES

When the history of the Cambridge Ring was discussed earlier in the book it was mentioned that a number of companies had adopted the technique as the basis for their local area networks. In most cases the method of data transport and transceiver functions are the same as those developed in the University of Cambridge Computer Laboratory. In summary these are:

Topology: A ring in which data always flows in the same direction.

Access techniques: Empty slot which circulates continuously and which can be used by any station. Once a station has placed data in that slot it is unable to send any more until the slot is returned to it, when the station must mark it as empty and pass it on. It is then free to use the next empty slot which is passed to it.

Hardware required: Repeaters must be placed at intervals (generally less than 100 metres apart) in order to regenerate the slots, check their parity and provide the means by which data can be placed on or read from the ring. Attached to the repeaters are devices which perform the logical functions of access and ring control, and which can interface to the end-user's equipment.

Power requirements: The repeaters are active elements in the ring and so they must be working all the time the ring is operational. To ensure this, power is normally taken directly from the ring although other methods are possible to isolate the repeaters should the power to them be cut off, provided that the distance between working repeaters is not too great.

Cable: Generally two pairs of twisted-pair cable are used, but this can vary from system to system. Different media can be mixed in the same ring. In fact the Cambridge Computer Laboratory ring contains a segment made from optic fibre.

Packet format: The ring packet format used at Cambridge was described earlier. In practice most suppliers of basic Cambridge Ring products have allowed for two packet types: one is the basic 38-bit format already described, the other is a 40-bit packet. This latter packet has two extra bits following the data field which are used to make the design and implementation of the higher-level protocols simpler.

Transmission speed: Practically every Cambridge Ring in operation works at a raw data transmission rate of 10 Mbps.

Protocols: Basic block, single shot and byte stream protocols are generally all supported.

All the companies with Cambridge Ring products are British. There are a large number of them, but the best known are discussed below.

Logica VTS – Polynet

Polynet is essentially a standard Cambridge Ring which can operate with either 38- or 40- bit ring packets. It uses three pairs of twisted-pair cable rather than two and repeaters operate from a lower voltage than the Cambridge installation. A number of interface units are available to connect well known mini- and microcomputer systems and terminals to the ring.

Orbis Computers Ltd

Orbis Computers Ltd was formed by one of the Cambridge University developers of the ring to manufacture a commercial version. As such, it uses the standard techniques developed at Cambridge.

Toltec Computer Ltd – DataRing

Toltec is another small company which supplies a near standard version of the Cambridge Ring. It is intended to use the 40-bit ring packet, but can be adapted to accept the 38-bit packet when used with equipment from other sources built to this standard. A limited number of interfaces are available.

Scientific and Electronic Enterprises Ltd – Transring 2000

This company (SEEL) has cooperated with the Edinburgh Regional Computing Centre to produce another near standard version of the Cambridge Ring, this time using 38-bit ring packets. Like Toltec and Logica VTS, SEEL can provide a limited number of interfaces to user equipment.

Most of the above suppliers can provide interface devices to the kinds of computer and terminal found in universities and other research establishments: eg DEC's PDP-11, LSI-11; S100 bus; and RS-232. This indicates the type of market which they serve. Other device interfaces could easily be developed and the market widened provided there is the demand.

Unlike bus-based networks, the Cambridge Ring is an ideal candidate for using optic fibres. Since the repeaters are the means to extract information as well as to regenerate the signal, their inclusion in the ring is essential and it is not difficult to construct repeaters which read in data from the optic fibre input, convert it to electrical signals for the station attached to it, and regenerate the light pulses for the next leg of the ring. A feature of optic fibres is their extremely low loss and distortion characteristics (hence few errors), so rings with optic fibres are not so limited in the distance apart allowed for the repeaters. Gaps of the order of a kilometre can easily be handled. However, the cost of optic fibres and their repeaters, and the limited life of some current laser transmitters, will limit their use in ring networks for the immediate future.

Another empty slot ring which differs considerably from the normal

Cambridge Ring is the *PLANET* network from the UK data communications company Racal-Milgo.

At the time of writing, details of the way PLANET operates are difficult to obtain but the following is known:

PLANET— stands for Private Local Area Network;

Medium – coaxial cable with impedance of 75 ohms, duplicated for back-up purposes;

Access method – empty slot which circulates continuously;

Ring packet – 42-bit packet containing 16 bits of data. The structure of the packet is different from the one normally used for the Cambridge Ring, and is not directly compatible;

Hardware – access to the ring cable itself is provided by passive access points. To these are connected active devices which provide an interface for up to two devices;

Protocols – PLANET uses a Network Administrator station to set up virtual circuits between end-user devices.

PLANET will provide facilities for two or more rings to be interconnected, and interfaces to public telecommunications networks will be available to allow access to and from remote rings and devices. The basic error detection used in empty slot rings is employed by PLANET and a break in the ring can be automatically bypassed by the Administrator selecting the back-up cable. The Administrator itself can be duplicated, in which case the network will automatically switch to the back-up machine if the usual one fails.

Although few details of PLANET are available it does seem that this is the sort of ring which will appeal to the average customer, rather than the basic building blocks provided by some other Cambridge Ring suppliers.

BROADBAND NETWORKS

Broadband local area networks all use radio frequency modulation techniques to transport the information around the network. Generally they elect to use the normal off-the-shelf CATV products which are readily available in the USA to service their extensive cable television industry.

The main problem until recently with broadband networks has been the high cost of providing the RF modems and interface units which are required, and also the limited number of channels which can be accommodated within the bandwidth of a single cable. This latter problem, together with the problems in switching RF modem carrier frequencies whenever there was the need to change channels (when wanting to converse with another host or user, for example), restricted the development of broadband networks until the contention bus ideas were applied. The resulting mixture of frequency division and carrier sense multiple access was discussed briefly when the systems developed by the Mitre Corporation were examined earlier. In this section we see how these are being developed as commercial systems.

Ungermann-Bass, who currently supply true Ethernet networks under the name Net/One, are known to be developing a system which uses Ethernet protocols on a broadband cable running at 5 Mbps. However, at the time of writing, no details of the system are known.

One of the longest-established broadband systems is Videodata, developed by Interactive Systems in the USA and marketed in the UK by 3M. Videodata originally used the technique of frequency division multiplexing to allocate discrete channels to pairs of users on a point-to-point basis. The modems were dedicated to one frequency band for data flow in one direction and another frequency for the reverse direction.

The Videodata system has since been developed to handle point-to-point, multidrop and distributed communications all within the confines of a single coaxial cable. Their main market is in the industrial and process control environments where the broadband technique has great advantages since it is relatively immune to interference caused by electrically noisy equipment.

The point-to-point system is the same as that already described. The multidrop option uses a headend modem which polls each of the attached systems in a manner typical of all polled multidrop configurations. Any system with data to send is allowed exclusive use of the channel. The distributed communications system is different from most other networks in that it uses one channel as a polling or control channel through which the headend polls all the other systems. If one of these wants to send data then it is assigned another channel for its exclusive use (seven are available). The modems on these systems must therefore be capable of operating on up to eight channels. The system is capable of expansion. By utilising frequency agile modems more than 100 channels could be used.

The whole Videodata system uses just one coaxial cable and divides the bandwidth up as follows:

— Forward channels: 5-108 MHz

— Return channels: 170-300 MHz

The Wang Laboratories have taken the MITRENET approach of using two separate coaxial cables and developed a product called Wangnet. Using two cables means that the full 300-400 MHz bandwidth is available for both forward and reverse channels since one cable is used for sending only and one used for receiving. Wangnet uses a system with 340 MHz bandwidth and splits this up into three discrete bands:

(1) *WANGBAND*

This band is intended for communications between Wang processors, typically Wang VS, OIS and 2200 systems. It uses a contention bus scheme (CSMA/CD) and operates at 12 Mbps. Packet formatting and transmission handling are performed in the Cable Interface Unit which interfaces the end system to the network.

(2) *INTERCONNECT BAND*

The interconnect band is used to interconnect terminals and non-Wang systems. It is itself split into three parts:

(a)   16 dedicated 64 kbps channels;

(b)   32 dedicated multipoint or point-to-point 9600 bps channels;

(c)   256 switched 9600 bps channels.

Options (a) and (b) require fixed frequency modems, whereas (c) requires frequency agile modems with autodial and keying facilities. The switched channels in option (c) are controlled by a device called the Wang Data Switch which polls the devices for call requests and then selects unused channels and switches the modems involved to use them.

(3) *UTILITY BAND*

The Utility Band is available for use with non-data services such as video, voice, conferencing, etc. Normally this channel will be divided up into 6 MHz segments as this is the amount real-time colour video requires.

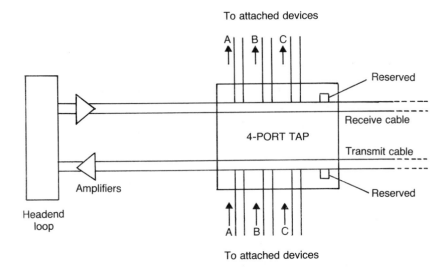

Figure 6.7   WANGNET

The general form of Wangnet is shown in Figure 6.7. The taps provided by Wang will normally be 4-port taps, although 4-, 6- and 8-port taps will be available. One of the ports is reserved. The rest are available for attached devices.

Another system which is being developed using broadband techniques is LocalNet from Sytek, a part of the Network Resources Corporation in the USA. This product is marketed in the UK by Network Technology Limited (NTL), part of the Information Technology Limited group. LocalNet uses a single standard CATV cable with 75 ohms impedance and utilising 300 MHz bandwidth. Two versions of LocalNet are produced: LocalNet 20, a fairly low-speed network; and LocalNet 40, a high-speed system; and plans are in hand for circuit switching.

Briefly their specifications are:

LocalNet System 20

— 120 channels of 300 kHz bandwidth, each capable of carrying 128 kbps;

— CSMA/CD access technique and sharing mechanism used for each channel;

— 200 active stations per channel;

— transmit band: 70-106 MHz;

— receive band: 226-262 MHz;

— a device is available to allow messages in one band to be sent to devices in another band;

— a user command language based on X.28 is available.

LocalNet System 40

— 5 channels of 2 Mbps each, 6 MHz wide and aligned on standard US television channel boundaries;

— CSMA/CD access method used;

— transmit band: 40-70 MHz;

— receive band: 196-226 MHz.

As can be seen, the two classes of LocalNet use different frequency bands and so they can run side-by-side using the same cable. Interface devices are available to bridge between System 20 and System 40 channels. In this way the new user can start with a cheap system based on System 20 and later extend it to System 40 without any need to scrap the original network. The packets sent through the network are similar to HDLC frames.

The most vulnerable part of this type of network is the headend device which, in the case of LocalNet, has to receive all transmissions on one band and retransmit them at a frequency 156 MHz greater. This device must be duplicated in a network in which reliability is especially important, because any failure in it renders the whole network unusable.

REGISTER INSERTION RINGS

Register insertion rings have been around in experimental form for a long time. The original implementation of the Cambridge Ring used register insertion, and this was based on one which was already working in the Berne laboratories of the Hasler telecommunications company.

Hasler were experimenting with a single multipurpose network for communications in a limited area but which was suitable for telephone (digitised), alarms, paging, control, etc, as well as data. Their studies began in 1970 and they eventually developed a product to serve these requirements called SILK (standing for System for Integrated Local Communications).

The technique for register insertion, originally described (reference 6.3), was to employ two registers in the access device on the loop. When the device has a packet to send, it loads it into one register and waits for a gap between packets passing round the loop. When one is reached, it switches the incoming line to a register or buffer, and the register containing the packet to be transmitted is switched to the outgoing line. Once the whole register has been emptied the outgoing line is switched to the buffer which has been connected to the incoming line and this buffer stays in series with the loop until the transmitted packet returns to the sender. As soon as it has all entered the delay buffer, the incoming and outgoing lines are again joined together so removing the delay buffer from one ring. This is shown in Figure 6.8.

Hasler modified this system in their practical SILK implementation (Figure 6.9). They use three buffers or registers. The delay buffer can be tapped at byte intervals which allows variable length packets to be used. Before a station has sent any data, the pointer is set to the start of the delay buffer, the loop bypassing it in effect. When a packet is ready to be transmitted it is loaded into the transmit register and the station waits for a gap in the packets on the loop. When one is detected it switches B to the transmit buffer and shifts the packet onto the outgoing line. Each new byte arriving from the loop during this time is stored in the delay buffer (which is also a shift register), the pointer moving one place to the right for each byte received. When the transmit register is empty, B is switched

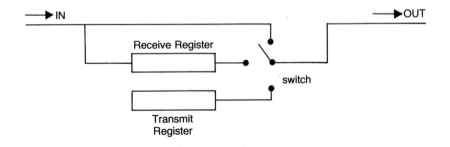

Figure 6.8   Basic Register Insertion Technique

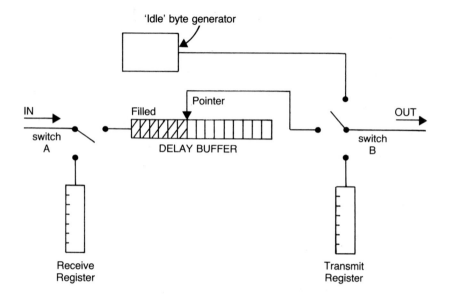

Figure 6.9   Hasler SILK Implementation of Register Insertion

back to the loop which now has the delay buffer in series. The pointer in the delay buffer stays in this position until 'idle' bytes (indicating no data) are received, in which case these are not stored but the pointer moves one place to the left for each idle byte received.

When a station receives a packet addressed to it, switch A directs the packet into the receive register whilst at the same time switch B takes 'idle' bytes from the 'Idle Byte Generator' rather than the delay buffer. When the whole packet has been received, the switches A and B revert to the delay buffer. Thus, in SILK, a packet does not travel round the whole loop but only goes from the sender to the receiver, where it is replaced by 'idle' bytes. Each station automatically removes idle bytes by not storing them in its delay buffer. A station cannot send out a packet unless the delay buffer has as much free space as the length of the packet.

To ensure adequate acknowledgement levels, higher levels of protocol are built on top of this system. For data transmission applications, Hasler have implemented CCITT recommendations X.21. Telephones can be attached to the ring through suitable interfaces and a large number of simultaneous conversations can be supported.

SILK employs a system of loop braiding to route round links or stations which have failed or are not switched on. A special monitoring station is needed in the network to check that packets are removed, rather than circulating for ever if the destination device is not listening. The monitoring station can also send out test packets, report errors, etc.

The ring, like most other rings, is unidirectional. It operates at 16.896 Mbps and normally uses ordinary 75 ohm coaxial cable. Because of the need for buffers and registers, the size of the ring packets is rather limited (16 bytes maximum), but this is of little concern to the user because of high levels of protocol provided.

The SILK network is interesting for a number of reasons. It is one of the few commercially available register insertion rings. It shows how several telecommunications needs can be handled by a simple single network. The choice of CCITT protocols for data connection and transmission is also interesting since these are the generally accepted standards which are used for connecting to the telecommunications network provided by the public authorities. Their use in a local area network shows that CCITT protocols can be applied in a more limited environment whilst gaining the advantages of advanced protocols to ensure reliable data transport.

TOKEN ACCESS SYSTEMS

By token access systems is meant that a special bit pattern called the token is sent out on the network and when a station wishes to transmit, it must first be given the token by another station. The transmitting station then holds on to the token whilst it transmits its data and then sends the token out as the last part of the information. Although token schemes can be implemented on either ring or bus networks, the technique is not well represented by commercial products yet but is of particular interest as it is one of the possible techniques considered suitable for standardisation.

The way in which token access works has been described in an earlier chapter. Here we will describe just one implementation of a token passing ring: the DOMAIN system from Apollo Computer Inc.

DOMAIN stands for Distributed Operating Multi-Access Interactive Network. It is an integrated set of hardware and software products intended for applications involving large amounts of program development and calculation for people such as professional engineers and designers. Each user has a personal computer system and these are linked together to share resources by means of a high-performance token-passing ring local area network.

The ring operates at a raw data transmission speed of 12 Mbps and uses coaxial cable as the medium, although other media such as optic fibres could be used. A conventional token passing technique is used in which a unique bit pattern circulates continuously round the ring. The sender node places its frame of information, which can include up to 1024 bytes of data, onto the network following it with the token. The destination node sets one bit in the destination address field to indicate to the sender that it is listening and copies the frame before passing it on.

At the end of the normal HDLC-like frame, following the check field, is another acknowledgement field. The destination node uses this to indicate to the sender whether or not the packet was received correctly or had an error. Another check field is used first for the acknowledgement field, and then follows the token.

The original sender of the frame removes the frame and then passes the token on to the next node.

Another, longer-established token passing ring is supplied by the minicomputer company PRIME Computer as part of their PRIMENET system of networks. The ring can be used to interconnect PRIME computers within a limited area; other techniques are used where the PRIMENET network extends over a wide area.

The ring operates at 8 Mbps and up to 16 systems can be interconnected with it, although in practice this is usually less. The node repeaters are automatically bypassed if that node is not switched on but the maximum distance allowed between *active* repeaters is 230 metres.

PRIMENET is intended only for interconnecting PRIME's own computers. Terminals and peripherals are attached to the network through their host computers, and through them they can access other services on the network.

OTHER SYSTEMS

Most local area networks in use fall broadly within one of the categories described in earlier sections of this chapter. However, a small number are available which differ in some significant manner and are worth mentioning briefly.

XIBUS and XINET

The most interesting in the UK are probably the XIBUS and XINET systems developed by a small British company called Xionics, and now marketed by Master Systems (Data Products) Ltd. The full title is XIBUS Electronic Office System, and this describes the market for which it is intended. XINET is the underlying local area network which is essential to the proper functioning of an electronic office system.

Briefly, XIBUS provides a wide range of services for the electronic office in the form of:

— *electronic filing* and retrieval using large capacity disks with both public and private files;

— *word processing,* including the production of paper copies;

— *electronic mail* both within the network and to other sites using telex and teletex (when it becomes available);

— *personal computing* using the XIBUS multi-function workstation which incorporates a microprocessor running a CP/M-like operating system;

— *external information sources* can be accessed through gateways;

— *integrated voice, image and data,* so that short voice messages can be appended to text, and images may be stored and transmitted.

The XINET local area network is a ring-shaped system operating at 10 Mbps using a 10-bit wide highway which is duplicated for reliability. Eight bits of the highway are used to transmit data a byte at a time as a parallel bit stream. The other two are used for clocking and parity. The size of the packets sent round the ring is large when compared with most other ring technologies, and they contain 240 bytes of data.

Workstations and other devices are connected to the ring by means of 'intelligent sockets'. Between them and the hosts or workstations are the communications adaptors necessary to perform the protocol handling and interfacing required.

The ring operates on the empty slot principle but differs in most respects from the normal Cambridge Ring. The emphasis in the XIBUS and XINET systems is not on a local area network but instead it is an integrated office system of which the network is only one part. Many large

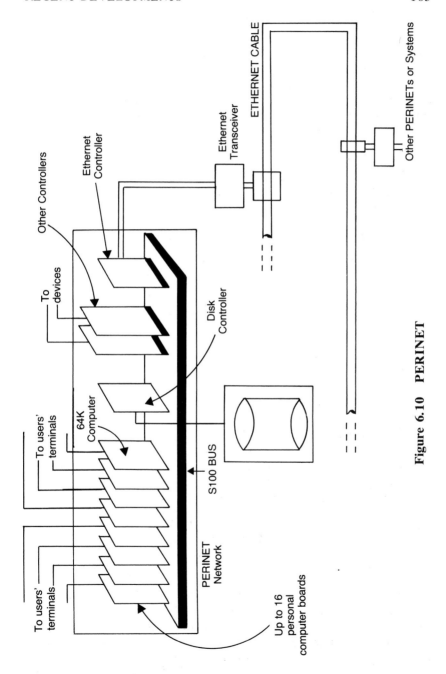

Figure 6.10 PERINET

and influential users in the UK have installed XIBUS and XINET, mostly on an experimental basis, and their experience seems to show that the system performs as intended.

PERINET

PERINET is a small local area network system developed by the UK company Perex Ltd, which is part of the SINTROM Group. It has two unusual features, both of which make it an interesting possibility for use in many environments.

The basic PERINET (Figure 6.10) is a set of single-board microcomputers contained within a single box and linked together by an S100 bus. Disk controllers, tape controllers, printers and control display can also be mounted on the S100 bus. Each user has a terminal which is connected to his own personal microcomputer board on the S100 bus using a dedicated cable. Up to 16 user systems are permitted on each bus. Each microcomputer is a 64K byte machine which uses a CP/M-compatible operating system. Thus the user has a personal microcomputer system which is linked to others, and to shared devices, through the PERINET system.

The other major characteristic of the network is the inclusion of a board to fit on the S100 bus which is a full Ethernet interface. In this manner each group of microcomputers on the bus can link, using the full 10 Mbps Ethernet, to other PERINET systems, Ethernet systems or gateways to other networks.

Incidentally, SINTROM is also the UK agent supplying Ethernet products from the US company 3 Com Corporation, which include Ethernet transceivers, cable, Q-Bus and Unibus controllers.

7 The PABX Approach

INTRODUCTION

An essential requirement of a local area network is that it should provide a simple to implement and cheap to install means of interconnecting as many users as possible within the local area. Most sites already have a very widespread communications network in the form of their telephone lines, so why not use this as the basis for a data communications network as well? At the centre of every telephone network is a telephone exchange which is capable of providing many more functions than is usual in a voice network.

Most office workers have access to a telephone close to their normal place of work, even if they do not have one on their own desk. It is becoming increasingly common to find the vast majority with their own telephone. Each telephone is connected by an exclusive line to the site exchange and through that to other users both on the same site and elsewhere using the public networks.

In most instances the telephone cables are grossly under-utilised since each is only used for a very small proportion of the day. The corresponding circuits and equipment in the exchanges are also not fully used. If the function of those cables, which have been installed over the years at a considerable cost, could be extended then this would appear to be a new ideal solution to local data communications needs. Since the lines and equipment are already used for speech it may seem that extending their use to include data could aid the integration of voice with data communications in the office: a long-term aim of many researchers into office procedures.

167

In this chapter we examine the possibilities of using the telephone-type of exchange and see how it can be extended to the data needs of the local area network.

A local telephone network is built round a local exchange so it is essentially an example of the more general star network. To put the PABX network into the context of data communications, the general star network will be discussed first.

STAR NETWORKS

A star-shaped network is well known both as a typical computer network (Figure 7.1a), in which the centre of the star is a computer system performing processing on information fed to it by the peripheral devices, and as a telephone system (Figure 7.1b), in which the central hub (the PABX) is a switch which interconnects the different users on the network. The first example illustrates the suitability of the star topology for the many-to-one approach, the second its use for interconnecting pairs of devices. It is less suitable where several spokes require concurrent access to a device on another spoke.

If we take the view that local area networks exist to provide on-site communications between computer-based devices, then the star network is by far the most dominant class around today, since most existing computer systems have on-line access facilities to one or more central computers. However, local area networks are typically thought of as providing interconnection between all the devices on the network, something which is not always present with the traditional computer-based networks. These networks typically operate by a device at the hub (which may be the computer itself or, more likely, a controller dedicated to handling terminals and peripheral devices) asking, or polling, each device in turn whether it has data to send. Only when the hub gives its permission can the devices on the spokes send the data. If the data is intended to go to another terminal, it is the usual practice in such systems for the computer at the hub to process the information and then send the message rather than just switching the incoming line to that of the receiver so that messages can pass through without being processed by the hub.

The star-shaped network is also typical of the local telephone system which most offices and sites have already installed. The hub in this case is the private telephone exchange which nowadays is usually an automatic device (a PABX – Private Automatic Branch Exchange) which allows

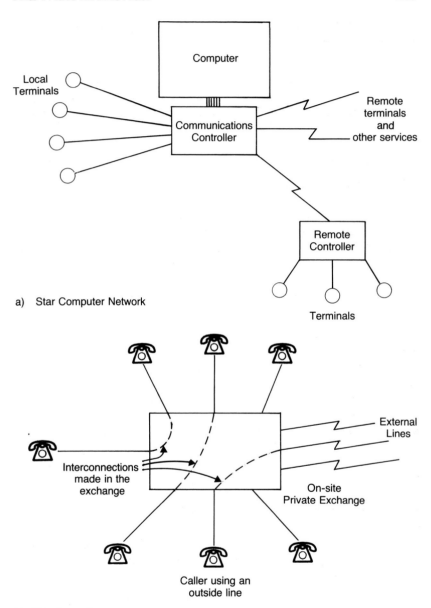

Figure 7.1   Star Networks

any telephone user to dial directly any other telephone connected to the same PABX. Frequently, facilities exist for any user to dial an external line which can then be used to make telephone calls to any other number on the public telephone systems. The PABX is a circuit switching device because, based on the dialling information it receives from the telephone making a call, it connects together the caller's line to that of the person being called. Once the circuit is made, it stays in existence until the conversation ends and the telephone receivers are replaced, which indicates to the PABX to break the circuit. Once a circuit joining two telephones exists, no other user can call either of them.

THE PABX AS A LOCAL AREA NETWORK

In the guise of the PABX, suitably enhanced, the star-shaped network is an important topology as a local area network.

PABXs are designed with the requirement of speech primarily in mind, but there is no obvious reason why the communications paths between subscribers should not be used for data as well since they already exist. The only real restrictions imposed are those due to bandwidth and noise on the communications channels. PABXs are normally designed for conversations which last a few minutes or so; if it takes several seconds to set up a call between subscribers this will be considered acceptable. For data requirements the call set-up time must be much less.

With the introduction of computer techniques and solid-state switching, the PABX can be made to provide the kind of facilities required in a computer network. Fast electronic switching allows circuits to be made and broken much quicker than is possible with the older type of exchange so that it is feasible to set up a circuit just to transfer a line of text from a terminal to a computer. It need only take a fraction of a second to set up the connection, transfer the information, and break the circuit again. The link to the computer is then available for another terminal to use. Modern PABXs can establish a circuit in less than half a second.

A PABX designed for handling data lines as well as speech needs extra equipment installed in it. The simplest case is shown in Figure 7.2. Calls are set up in the same manner as for speech telephones. The data terminal is connected to a *Data Terminal Adaptor* which has some mechanism for dialling another subscriber. The mechanism is generally an ordinary dial or a keypad. Within the PABX, special line handling equipment for data circuits is needed, called *Data Line Units*. Generally these can handle

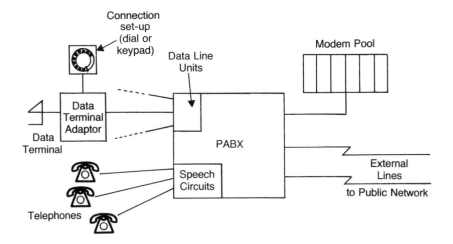

Figure 7.2   A PABX Capable of Handling Data Lines

digital data transmission rates of 64 kbps. If the data terminals are going to be connected over public networks to other systems then modems will also be needed. Rather than provide a modem for every such user, the PABX will have a Modem Pool which is shared. Whenever a data terminal requests an outside line, a modem from the modem pool will be selected by the PABX and switched into the outside line.

Another, more advanced, implementation is shown in Figure 7.3. In this the Data Terminal Adaptor and the Data Line Unit are enhanced to remove the need for a separate dialling unit. The connection to another subscriber is achieved by the Data Line Unit itself using commands sent by the data terminal user.

In both the examples just discussed the main part of the PABX is essentially the same as would be provided for handling speech only.

Modern digital PABXs can handle remote concentrators and multi-plexers, each of which in turn serves several subscribers. Figure 7.4 shows an example of a modern in-house telephone system which has the additional facilities to handle data on the same lines as the speech (subscriber multiplexed). The subscriber on one link can use both his telephone and the data terminal at the same time. Each device is handled separately at the exchange, so the data terminal could be connected to a computer

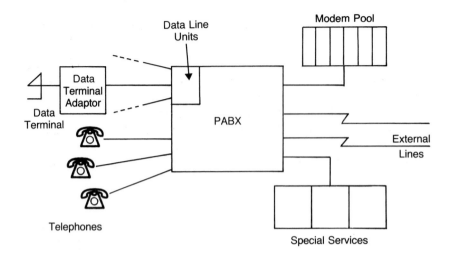

Figure 7.3   PABX Network with Enhanced Data Handling

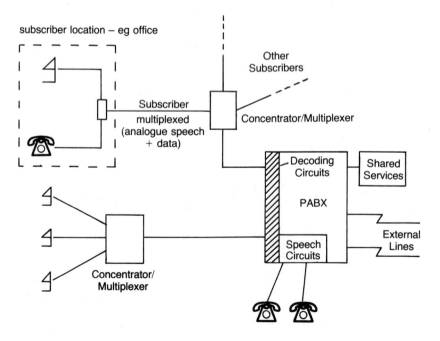

Figure 7.4   Advanced PABX Network with Multiplexing

service, for example, whilst still allowing the telephone to be used in the normal way.

The technique of employing remote devices to concentrate the information flow from several subscribers onto a limited number of exchange lines can be extended to handle remote networks. Figure 7.5 shows how the remote multiplexer/concentrator could be replaced by a local area network node which acts as a gateway between the PABX network and the local area network. Depending on the type of local area network employed, this node could be a network controller or just a gateway.

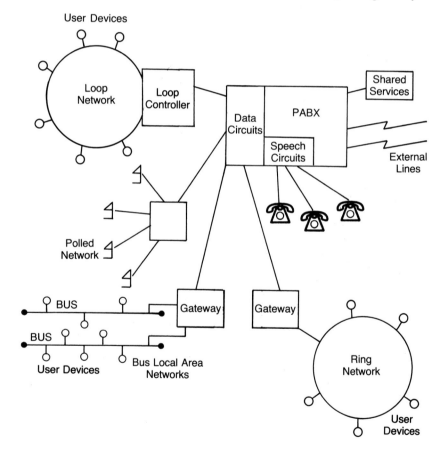

Figure 7.5   Integration of Local Area Networks into PABX Network

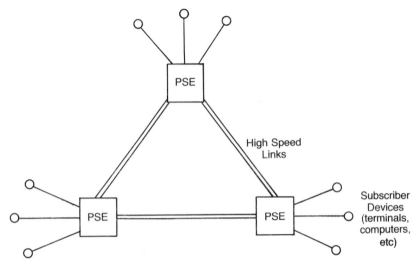

PSE: Packet Switching Exchange

Figure 7.6   Packet Switched Network

Although circuit switching is the traditional technique employed for the hub in the PABX-type of network, it is possible for it to operate as a packet switching exchange.

Packet switching has in recent years been adopted as the normal method for transporting data over public data networks. Public data networks can be compared with public telephone networks since both are networks which serve a large community of users and utilise an under-lying performance network which all the users share. Public packet switched data networks (Figure 7.6) use a number of exchanges situated at various places throughout the country, and all the users are connected to their nearest exchange. The exchanges themselves are interconnected by highly reliable high-speed circuits. Messages originating at a user site are broken down into conveniently sized blocks and put in a 'packet' which has the addresses of both the sender and the receiver. Packets are passed one by one to the packet switching exchange which sends them, interleaved with others from other users, to the exchange serving the destination device. Missing packets are checked for and those reaching the destination device are checked for transmission errors. Packets in error or missing are requested to be re-sent. Eventually the message is reassembled by the receiver or by the local exchange.

Although packet switching networks generally use more than one exchange, the concept can work just as well with a single one situated at the hub of a star network. Each device on the spokes can easily be in conversation with a number of different devices simultaneously, the interleaved packets travelling along the spoke being associated with different dialogues. This makes the technique especially suitable for stars which have one or more computer systems in the network.

The PABX at the centre of a network can perform functions other than normal line or message switching. For example, the PABX can provide conversions between the data transmission speed of the sender and that required by the receiver. The sending and destination devices may also operate using different communication protocols and character sets. The PABX can act as a protocol converter so allowing a terminal from one manufacturer to work successfully with a computer system from another. Protocol converters can be services shared by everyone connected to the PABX.

One of the most significant aspects of a star network is the fact that much of the intelligence needed to control the network can reside in the one place and be shared by all the devices in the system. This enables dumb terminals to be used directly in the network, with each one operating at any speed it likes. No special logic is required to gain access to the circuits since each of the links is usually dedicated to the one device. It is conceivable, although not frequently encountered, that different media could be used for the links between the devices at the end of the spokes and the hub. For example, twisted-pair cable could be used for some links, coaxial and ribbon cables for others, and even fibre optics if the application demanded it. The modern PABX can easily be made to incorporate features of this kind.

The hub software could also provide a high degree of security protection to prevent unauthorised persons from using the network, or unauthorised terminals from accessing certain computer systems. If a link or end device develops a fault, it is easy to identify which spoke the fault is on and report it to the network supervisor and disconnect it if necessary. Addressing is also simplified as each spoke corresponds to a particular device.

Modern PABXs often use *stored program control* (SPC) to provide a wide range of services which were not possible with the older design of electromechanical exchange designed for analogue use. Typically the facilities provided by SPC exchanges are:

— a call can be automatically redirected to another number if the dialled number is engaged, does not answer, or if the person associated with it has moved to another number;

— extensions can be dialled directly;

— certain numbers can be restricted;

— extension numbers can be changed easily so that a person can retain his own telephone number even when changing offices;

— traffic can be measured and recorded;

— fault location and diagnosis facilities can be provided;

— telephone conferencing with more than two subscribers being involved is possible.

With facilities like these the cost of a new digital SPC PABX can often be justified on the speech facilities alone. With suitable extensions, the PABX can be made to handle data, as described earlier. The advantage is obvious: the data terminals and computers can use the cables and ducts provided for the telephones – often one of the more costly items of the installation.

It must be recognised that, despite its advantages, the installation of a PABX controlled local area network may not always be the best solution. The PABX itself, by virtue of the intelligence it requires to control even the simplest network, is going to be quite a costly item. If there is an adequate PABX already installed for the telephone services it could be difficult to justify its replacement with a PABX for both voice and data, or indeed the installation of another for data alone.

The PABX is also quite vulnerable to failures since it must contain significant quantities of software to perform its functions properly. Advocates of the PABX approach point to the high reliability required and achieved (for example, by means of essential circuits being duplicated) for normal PABXs, and reason that the computerised ones will have to be as good if they are to replace the existing ones. However likely the hub PABX is to fail, the possibility of it happening is sufficient to deter many users who have the need for a very reliable data transmission network. Failure of the hub, whether this is a computer system, a circuit or packet switch or an advanced **PABX**, will stop the system performing as a network. If a network is being heavily loaded, the central control circuits and software can also become overloaded causing significant delays in setting up a call.

The cable network required by a star network is simple to visualise but generally difficult and costly to install when a large number of devices are being served. If the actual existing telephone cables can be used to handle data devices at an adequate speed without preventing the telephone itself from being used at the same time, then this problem is not serious. If new cables are required then each device will need a separate line to the centre.

Summarising the features of the star-shaped local area network based on the **PABX**, the following are the main advantages and disadvantages:

Advantages

— ideal for many-to-one configurations;

— suited to dumb terminals as well as intelligent ones;

— mixed transmission media and speeds can be used on the spokes;

— each spoke is independent of the rest;

— high security is possible;

— easy fault detection and isolation;

— addressing is easy, and is centrally controlled;

— cost can often be justified for voice alone;

— integration of data and voice (integration of office information handling) is possible;

— total network bandwidth can be very high (several hundred Mbps);

— a fairly large area can be covered (up to 3 km between device and hub).

Disadvantages

— vulnerable to central hub failures;

— complex technology required at the hub – hence expensive (although this is shared by all the subscribers making the cost per user very competitive);

— ports are needed at the hub to handle all the lines – either on a one-to-one basis or shared;

— laying cables and altering their routes can be expensive;

— to obtain all the benefits, the newest technology must be used, with its associated risk factor;

— the data rates which can be handled are generally slower than ring or bus topologies due to the hub processing required – 64 kbps typical, per channel.

OTHER POSSIBILITIES

Before leaving the description of the star and PABX-based local area network it is worth mentioning some of the other possibilities which have been suggested based on the central hub idea.

Illustrated in Figure 7.7 is the so-called star-shaped ring. In this, interconnections between devices at any one time are by means of a ring, the features of which are discussed elsewhere. But, every so often the ring

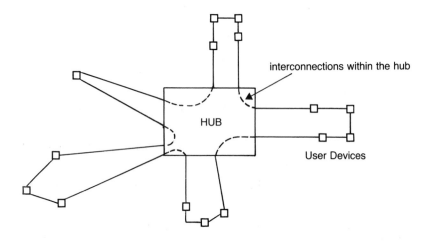

Figure 7.7   Star-Shaped Ring

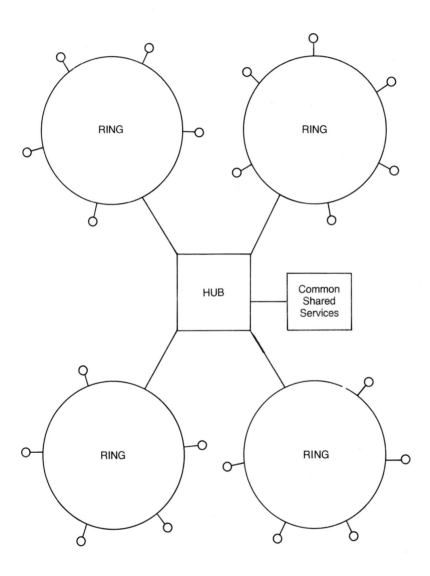

Figure 7.8   Rings Connected as a Star Network

passes through a central device which can either be unintelligent or intelligent. The unintelligent device just provides the facility to detect and isolate faulty sections of the ring, probably by manual means. If a small amount of intelligence is used then the control device could also perform as a ring monitor station. A well designed hub with considerable intelligence could be made by including hardware and software to continuously monitor each of the loops and to automatically switch out those which are troublesome. The ring configuration and order in which data passes from device to device could also be changed very easily. The last feature also enables new devices to be added to the ring without disturbing any users except those on the loop where the new device is being sited.

Further developments of the idea can be envisaged to allow the individual loops to be essentially separate rings (Figure 7.8) with the hub device common to all. The individual rings could operate at different speeds with the hub performing the conversions necessary when a device on one ring sends information to a device on another.

CONCLUSIONS

A network based on the intelligent PABX can perform as a local area network in some circumstances but it may be most important in the future as the link between different networks for speech, local data communications and off-site networks. The PABX may become the gateway between them all.

The PABX and local area network can be thought of as complementary, each enhancing the value of the other. A local area network is useful for communications within its own strictly limited community. Using a PABX, one local area network can access other local area networks, other data networks (the in-house data processing network being one obvious example), and the voice network. The PABX can also provide the means to subdivide the network into more manageable parts so that one section can be isolated from the other for development, diagnostic and maintenance purposes. If a PABX is part of several local area networks then services which are needed occasionally by users of the networks, such as traffic analysis and error-tracing, could be a service provided by the PABX and shared by everybody.

One question which has been asked, and which it is premature to answer yet, is whether local area networks, suitably enhanced, could perform the functions of the PABX. Could, for example, a special server device be placed on a local area network which can perform the circuit or message switching functions of a traditional PABX? In fact, could the PABX functions be distributed to all the devices on the network in the same manner that the functions of the packet switching exchange are distributed in a normal local area network ? The answer to both questions is definitely 'yes'. The technology is available now which can perform these functions, but more experience is needed of handling voice traffic on a local network with no central switch before the possibilities can be examined further. Until then most organisations should consider that PABXs and local area networks as we know them today will co-exist, but with a little thought they can be used in a complementary manner.

8 The Standards Situation

INTRODUCTION

Local area networks may not appear to be one of the most promising topics to standardise. After all, one of the early attractions of local networking was the desire to provide a communications technique which was free from the constraints typical of normal telecommunications. Computing as a whole has not been a very successful area for standards. Generally the standards that have been agreed have followed many years behind the products and have therefore been modelled upon the market leader as much as possible for there to be any chance of them succeeding. Possibly with this past experience of computer standards in mind, attention was turned to standards for local area networks very soon after it was realised that products would soon be flooding onto the market.

Both the suppliers of local area networks, computer equipment and electronic office products, and their customers stand to benefit from early standards. Buyers will not want to install a local network only to find that a limited number of items of user hardware can be used with it because the suppliers of the network have provided the wrong interface, or that manufacturers of the equipment which will be attached to it have not yet designed the necessary hardware and software. Customers are going to buy local area networks which have the greatest support amongst all the relevant suppliers.

These suppliers of computer and office equipment are also keen on supporting standards for local area networks because they wish to avoid developing a large and expensive set of interfaces to enable their products to be used with each network on the market.

Early and appropriate standardisation should encourage the growth of a market and more products for local area networks. The costs of the interfaces between the devices to be attached and the network itself will also be lower if there are standards, since the development costs will be lower and the volume of production higher.

The Xerox Corporation in the US was one of the first to develop both a local area networking technique (Ethernet) and some products for the office environment which use it. To help Ethernet become widely accepted, and to protect research investment, Xerox allied itself with two other companies (DEC and Intel) with different markets who were also in a position to benefit from the widespread use of local area networks. During 1980 this consortium produced Ethernet specifications which were made generally available to any other manufacturer. Shortly afterwards, the Institute of Electrical and Electronic Engineers (IEEE) in the US decided to put their weight behind a standardisation effort for local area networking. Naturally much of the input came from Xerox, DEC and Intel, but other interested parties became involved.

Work on network standards for industrial and process control applications (Proway) has been underway for several years and when the interest in local area networks suddenly mushroomed during 1980 it was realised that Proway was a kind of local network and should be taken into consideration.

These are the three most significant items being considered now in local area networks. All concentrate on the lower-level data transmission requirements: the way strings of data can be transported from their source to their destination. At present very little effort has been applied to the application-oriented protocols which will be required in most environments to ensure that the strings of data, once they have been delivered successfully, can be understood and formatted into proper conversations.

The other important area of computer networking being standardised at this time is Open Systems Interconnection. This is concerned not only with the basic data transport mechanism but also with the applications using networks and the services which are needed to support them. In particular, one of the aims of the Open Systems Interconnection work is to ensure that a network of computer-based equipment from a number of different suppliers can be successfully put together. In this aspect the project has much in common with the aims of the designers of local area networks. For this reason, local networking standards are being aligned with those of the Open Systems Interconnection work. To put the other standards into context, Open Systems Interconnection is discussed first, followed by details of the current local area network standardisation effort.

OPEN SYSTEMS INTERCONNECTION

The ideal situation with regard to communications between computers and associated devices is that each should be able to send understandable messages to any other regardless of the make or internal design of the devices involved. Until recently this has been practically impossible but the current work on open systems interconnection standards aims to rectify the situation.

Traditional computer systems were closed; ie the computers, terminals, peripherals and other devices connected to them were all made to conform to rules which varied from system to system. The block size of the messages, the control characters used, the transmission mode, speed, etc, were all dictated by the major item in the system. Frequently these parameters were set by the supplier, although in a few special cases a user would design his own communications software. The situation was acceptable in the case where all the users and devices involved belonged to the same organisation, and where a limited choice of hardware was involved. Now more computing devices are being purchased by a wider range of users than before, many more new makes of computer are being put on the market, more office and industrial equipment incorporates computing devices than before, and interconnection of equipment is more important.

Another important factor contributing to the trend towards computing with communications is the development in the past few years of public data networks. Their most significant feature in this context is the fact that they are switched. Thus, connections between devices on the network need not be permanent or semi-permanent. At one moment a terminal can be interacting with one computer, and at the next moment, without anyone having to physically change any wiring, the same terminal could be sending data to another computer on the network. Under these circumstances, each device on the network has the potential for being accessible (ie open) to every other using the network.

Openness implies no *technical* hindrances to the exchange of information, but any system is quite capable of imposing its own means of limiting access to only selected systems and users. Openness, in this sense, is new to computing although in many other areas, such as the telephone service, the concept is accepted and well understood.

If users of computing devices are going to make full use of the opportunities for interconnection that local area, circuit and packet switched networks offer then open agreements are needed, not just at the level of being able to interface to the network, but also at the level of being able to exchange information. Agreements on the symbols, formats and sequences to use for messages are needed. Thus, the essential requirement of open systems working is a set of standards for communications protocols at all levels.

Interworking

Interconnection allows two or more users to be connected together in order to exchange data, but interworking demands that these users agree to observe the same rules in order that they may understand the data and can cooperate to perform some task.

Three essential ingredients are needed for two or more computers, terminals or other network users to be able to interwork:

(a)   A physical data transmission network to which all participating subscribers can connect.

   The purpose of a data transmission network is to transmit data reliably, and preferably also cheaply and quickly, between partners. It should be easy to use and should not involve the user in complex procedures for interfacing to it. Local area networks fall within this.

(b)   Compatible dialogues

   Each user of the data network should be able to understand what his partner is saying. To do this, each must adopt the same conventions, ie protocols.

(c)   Applications

   Within the typical office or factory it is very unlikely that all the terminals, workstations, computers, printers, etc, will be made by

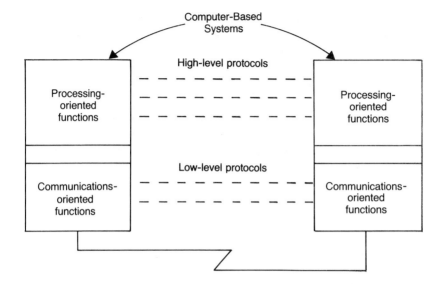

Figure 8.1   Layering Computer Communications Systems

the same company, and yet they must be used together. In the wider context, personnel records, purchasing and planning systems, for example, may be implemented by each of the individual divisions of the organisation, but they need to be interconnected for corporate planning and other purposes.

Interworking requirements can be roughly divided or layered into processing-oriented functions and communications-oriented functions (see Figure 8.1). The processing-oriented functions are concerned with the ability of two systems to exchange information and to understand it. The rules required to achieve this cooperation are called *high-level protocols*. The communications-oriented functions are concerned with the use of the physical data transmission network and the rules associated with its use are the *low-level protocols*.

The Reference Model

The basic model for open systems interconnection has been developed by the International Organization for Standardization (ISO) (described in detail in reference 8.1). Using it, Open Systems Interconnection (OSI) can be defined as:

> 'standardised procedures for the exchange of information among systems which are accessible to one another for this purpose by virtue of their mutual use of these procedures'.

The purpose of OSI is for any one user of a communications network to be able to communicate and work with any other. Ideally each one should not need to know the technical characteristics (eg computer types) of any other. All he really needs to know is that the others observe the same conventions.

The Reference Model of OSI was developed to provide a common basis for the coordination of standards development in the area, while allowing existing standards to be placed in perspective. It is intended that the model should provide a common reference for maintaining consistency of all related standards. The model does not define precisely the services and protocols of the interconnection architecture but it does identify the areas where such standards should exist.

The idea of layering was introduced in the discussion of high- and low-level protocols to divide up the interworking model into processing- and communications-oriented functions. The ISO Reference Model for OSI (shown in Figure 8.2) uses seven layers to simplify the work of defining all the protocols and services required for interworking. This allows separate teams of experts to work independently on developing standards for each layer.

Each layer is as self-contained as possible and, in defining its functions, only the interfaces to the immediately adjacent layers, together with the services provided by the lower layers, need to be known.

Two users in separate systems but in the same layer communicate with each other using protocols appropriate to their layer (the peer-to-peer protocols). It appears to them that they are conversing directly but in fact they are using the lower layers to achieve this.

Referring again to Figure 8.2, the Physical Medium which joins the two systems (shown diagrammatically at the base of the figure) needs explanation. Examples are the public telephone network, leased lines or a public switched data network such as PSS. The boundary in these cases is the CCITT-defined boundary between the data circuit-terminating

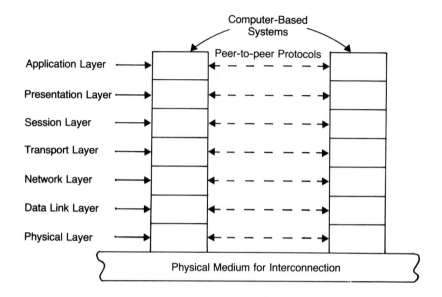

Figure 8.2 ISO Seven-Layer Reference Model

equipment (a modem for example) and the data terminal equipment (the subscriber's computer or terminal). The Physical Medium could also be a local area network. Any combination of public or private network can be used to interconnect open systems.

Briefly the functions of each of the layers are as follows:

— *Physical Layer*

This provides the means to interface to the physical medium, and the way to control its use.

— *Data Link Layer*

In recognising that physical transmission media are subject to random faults and noises, data link protocols were introduced some time ago to enable transmission errors to be detected and corrected. High-Level Data Link Control (HDLC) is a typical example. The Data Link Layer of the ISO model is concerned with these functions.

— *Network Layer*

This layer is required to provide the means to exchange data between systems using the network. In particular it performs the routeing and switching operations associated with establishing and operating a logical connection between systems. The Network Layer also performs the very valuable gateway function of linking two separate networks when these are being used to connect two end systems.

— *Transport Layer*

The Transport Layer provides, in association with the layers below it, a universal transport service which is independent of the physical medium in use. Users of the transport service request a particular class and quality of service and the Transport Layer is responsible for optimising the available resources to provide this service.

The quality is concerned with data transfer rate, residual errors and associated features, whilst the classes cover the various different types of traffic which diverse applications require (eg batch and transaction processing).

— *Session Layer*

The Session Layer establishes logical communication paths between applications wishing to exchange data. These two applications form a liaison for this purpose, called a session. The Session Layer maintains this liaison and ensures that data reaching a system is routed to the correct application. It also ensures that the information exchanged is correctly synchronised and delimited so that, for example, two applications do not try to transmit to each other simultaneously unless full-duplex working is allowed.

— *Presentation Layer*

The Presentation Layer performs the two-way function of taking information from applications and converting it into a form suitable for common understanding (ie not machine dependent), and also presenting the data exchanged between systems to the applications in a form they can understand. The layer provides services which can give independence of character representation, command format and, most importantly, independence of machine characteristics.

— *Application Layer*

The highest layer defined by the ISO Reference Model is concerned with supporting the applications which exchange information with others. Many different types of application are relevant to OSI, from terminal to computer transaction processing to interconnected real-time process control programs. Some of the protocols associated with this layer will be concerned with particular types of application, others will be for general application support.

Using the Reference Model

The Reference Model by itself does not provide a standard for interworking of systems but, given a stable model, the standards which are needed can be developed and fitted together within the framework it defines. It is not yet itself a full standard although most workers in the area now consider it to be stable enough for other standards to be developed. Work is now proceeding on the development of OSI standards in the following areas:

— virtual terminal protocols;

— file transfer, access and management protocols;

— job transfer and manipulation protocols;

— session layer services and protocols;

— transport layer services and protocols;

— network layer services and protocols;

— data link layer services and protocols;

— physical layer services and protocols;

— OSI management protocols.

The first three items relate to the Application and Presentation Layers and it is hoped that experience gained in their development will lead to general service and protocol standards for the Presentation Layer. The OSI management protocols relate mainly to the Application Layer. (Further details can be found in reference 8.2.) Local area network standards are concerned more with the Network, Data Link and Physical Layers.

ISO WORK ON LOCAL AREA NETWORKS

The International Organization for Standardization (ISO) has concentrated much of its effort in computer communications on Open Systems Interconnection (OSI) and related protocols, including the High-Level Data Link Control (HDLC) protocol for data links. Little effort has been spent on standards explicitly for local area networks. Most of the work has been on ensuring that the OSI reference model can accommodate the different requirements of local networking.

The OSI reference model was conceived as a model for computer networking primarily in the point-to-point or packet switched situation. When applied to the local networking concept some modifications will be required. One major difference between a local network and a traditional computer network is that in the former case blocks of information may be delivered to a destination from a number of different sources within a short time interval. The OSI reference model is generally built around the assumption that the sender and receiver of a block of information will first of all enter into an agreement about exchanging information, the format of the blocks and manner of their exchange. The exchange is generally one-to-one or one-to-many. A local area network is a many-to-many situation, and in most implementations every device on the network hears the transmissions from every other device, regardless of their destination. Some procedure must be built into the devices to extract messages addressed to them and ignore the rest.

The standard OSI reference model is often said to be 'connection-oriented', by which is meant to imply that the end-points are bound together in an exclusive one-to-one liaison to ensure sequenced block transfer. Local area networks require a 'connectionless' service in which there is no prior agreement or knowledge about where the next block of information is coming from. For this reason it makes sense to build a modified reference model which is particularly suited to local networking, but which can also accommodate the more established form of computer network.

Figure 8.3 shows the form such a model may take. In the OSI reference model the lowest layer, the Physical Layer, interfaces to the physical media, which can be the data circuit-terminating equipment (DCE),

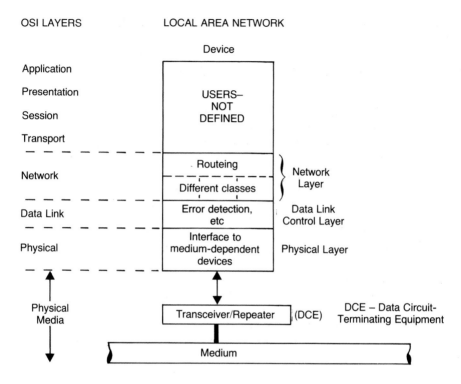

Figure 8.3   Reference Model for Local Area Networks

which is the CCITT's name for a modem or device which interfaces to the transmission network. For a local area network the DCE will usually be a transceiver or repeater, which in turn is attached to the medium being used. The Physical Layer of the Local Area Network Reference Model will perform the same type of interface functions as those defined for the OSI model. In most cases the physical medium in the local network will support only bit-serial transmission. One of the tasks of the Physical Layer will be to take the blocks of data given to it by the Data Link Layer and put these into a serial form for transmission.

The Data Link Layer has to perform the usual function of system-to-system error detection and correction. In addition a different type of flow control must be used to avoid network congestion in systems where this can be a problem. This layer may, on request, provide different qualities of service: eg sequencing, end-to-end flow control and connectionless transmission.

The Network Layer of a Local Area Network Architecture should be able to handle different classes of service: eg virtual circuits, datagrams, broadcasting, transaction processing, etc. Because it is unlikely that every local network will operate in complete isolation, the Network Layer must also provide the functions for handling transfers from one local network to another, or from a wide area network to a local network. It should provide a service to the upper levels which masks the features of the underlying media.

The Transport Level is outside the parts of the Reference Model which are specific to local networking. Its purpose is to provide an end-to-end transport service to the users' applications or devices which are in the source and destination systems. The only modification needed is that of permitting a connectionless mode of operation so that messages may be sent without sequencing or prior agreements between the applications at the source and destination.

At the time of writing, this work in ISO is at an early stage and will undoubtedly be influenced very significantly by later developments by the IEEE and by proprietary systems.

IEEE STANDARDS WORK

The American Institute of Electrical and Electronic Engineers (IEEE) Computer Society in February 1980 formed its Local Network Standards Committee, Project 802. A document has been published (reference 8.3) which sets out the scope of the standards work being attempted. Figure 8.4 shows the basic form of the model used to describe a local area network and the associated parts of the system connected to it. It is intended that the standards shall define the physical interfaces and services listed below:

(1)   The service provided by the Link Layer L to the upper layers (generally defined by the OSI reference model).

(2)   The data link protocol ($L \longleftrightarrow L$).

(3)   The interface between the Link Layer and the Physical Layer P' in the attached device.

(4)   The signalling protocol between the attached device and the Medium Access Unit (P'P).

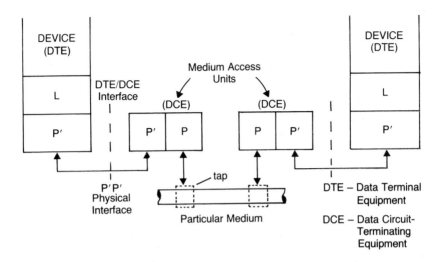

Figure 8.4   IEEE Model for Local Area Networks

(5) The physical interface P'P' between the attached device and the Medium Access Unit.

(6) A protocol P'P.

(7) A signalling protocol PP.

(8) The physical interface to the medium itself, ie the way the actual cable is tapped.

The overall objective of the IEEE Local Network Standard is to promote compatibility between equipment made by different manufacturers such that data communication can take place between equipment with the minimum effort on the part of the users or the builders of a system containing the equipment.

The standard is intended to be applicable to many different environments, topologies, applications and services. At present the following services are being specially considered: file transfer, graphical data, text, computer-generated data, electronic mail, monitoring and control information, measurement and control of processes. Digitised voice traffic is expected to be considered at a later stage. The standard is also intended to be used with most computer-based devices: computers, terminals, mass storage devices, printers, plotters, electronic copiers, measuring instruments, control equipment and gateway devices to other networks.

One important aim of the work is to insulate the end-user and the attached device from the particular characteristics (topology, access mechanism and medium) of the underlying network. How this is achieved will be discussed later.

The Committee is subdivided into 3 subcommittees:

(1) *Media*
The media subcommittee is concerned with the physical media used by the networks, the characteristics of the data being transported, the details of the Physical Layer and its interface to the Data Link Layer.

(2) *Data Link and Media Access Control (DLMAC)*
The DLMAC subcommittee is concerned with the data link protocols, the control protocols used in accessing the physical media (including addressing and framing) and the interfaces to the Physical and Network Layers.

(3) *High-Level Interface*
The High-Level Interface subcommittee is working on the higher level protocols used by the attached devices and is matching the particular requirements of a local area network with the five upper layers of the OSI reference model.

The whole set of protocols, interfaces and services correspond as far as possible with the architecture set out in the ISO Open Systems Interconnection Reference Model. Special consideration is being given to the need, in this environment, to implement the protocols as cheaply as possible, with due consideration given to the fact that local networks will often be used to interconnect inexpensive devices.

The network data transmission rates currently being considered are within the range 1 - 20 Mbps. The network defined should also be capable of supporting at least 200 devices, and its minimum length should be 2 km, with or without repeaters. There is no restriction on the topologies supported. Nor should the standards preclude networks with special requirements for prompt delivery, such as voice, measurement and industrial control applications.

The general structure used by the IEEE in defining the standards is shown in Figure 8.5. The functions of the various layers are as follows:

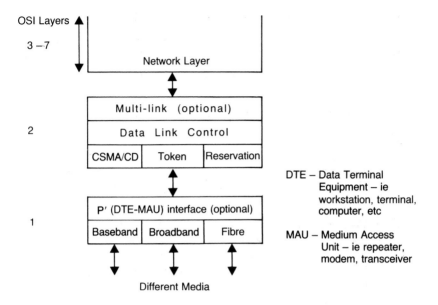

Figure 8.5   IEEE Local Area Network Structure

— *Network Layer*

The Network Layer in a local area network is primarily concerned with providing a media- and access mechanism-independent interface to the upper layers in the architecture of the attached device. Its other function is to decide on the route the packets of data will follow on the next stage of their journey. This is especially relevant where the device concerned is a gateway, a multiplexer or a message or packet switch.

— *Multi-Link Sub-Layer*

The Multi-Link Sub-Layer is an optional part of the Data Link Layer and it applies to devices which support more than one link protocol, eg a switch or a gateway.

— *Data Link Control Sub-Layer*

The Data Link Control Sub-Layer is the part of the Data Link Layer which provides the usual data link protocol functions of

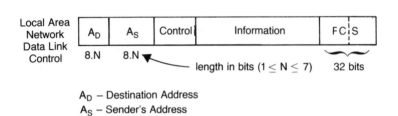

A_D — Destination Address
A_S — Sender's Address

Figure 8.6   Comparison of HDLC and Local Network Frames

framing, addressing, formatting, etc, in a form which is independent of the access mechanism, topology and physical medium in use. Although High-Level Data Link Control (HDLC) was specified as the standard to aim for, it was realised that in a local network some alterations would be necessary, but the same overall function and method of operation as HDLC have been retained. Figure 8.6 shows the HDLC and the Local Network Data Link Control (LNDLC) frames. Note that LNDLC does not need to use delimiting flags since the frame preamble and carrier used on local networks are sufficient to delimit the frame. Also, because some local network access techniques require the detection of collisions to be made, the frame check (FCS) field can be twice as long to improve error detection. In addition the source and destination addresses are both needed. Further levels of addressing are possible by means of group and broadcast address bits in the ordinary address fields.

— *CSMA/CD, Token and Reservation Access Sub-Layer*

The media access sub-layer has parts which are specific to the different techniques used. At the time of writing, only CSMA/CD and the Token methods of access had been considered in depth. CSMA/CD is applicable only to bus topology, but Token access can be used on buses or rings, although work has concentrated on the bus. Both CSMA/CD and Token access techniques have been described in detail elsewhere in the book.

— *P' Interface to the Medium Access Unit*

The Medium Access Unit (MAU) is the device responsible for transmitting and receiving frames of data on the medium. It generally consists of two parts: a transceiver/coupler/modem and a cable tap. This sub-layer is optional, only being needed when the transceiver is not integrated into the DTE (ie the attached device). In the case where it is integrated, no explicit external interface at this point is required.

— *P Interfaces*

Of the possible media specified, interest has been concentrated on baseband coaxial cable. The methods of interfacing to the different media vary so much that one single interface is not possible.

The IEEE work began by concentrating on the CSMA/CD technique because of the very considerable experience which was available using Ethernet, but it soon become evident that this had too little general support in the computer community for it to become a general standard. It was agreed that CSMA/CD was simple to implement and performed well under light loads, but it had the problem that no maximum time for access could be guaranteed which made it unsuitable for high-priority devices in critical situations (eg process control). This, together with the other problems of limited network size, packet length and difficulty in pin-pointing defects in the network, led to the adoption of an alternative standard: token passing. It may seem strange that a standard should include two totally different and incompatible options, but such was the pressure from both sets of adherents that this was found to be the only possible option. It also reflects rather vividly the range of uses possible for local area networks and the inability of a single system to serve all the needs.

Token passing does not limit the maximum size of the packets, and it is very suitable for critical situations in which a node must be guaranteed access to the network. It is, however, much more complex to implement although IEEE have been assured that it can be done using microelectronics in a single cheap package.

Although the CSMA/CD option of the IEEE work was based on Ethernet it has diverged from the Ethernet specification originally published. Efforts have been made to resolve the differences. At the time of writing, none of the IEEE proposals had become standards.

The American National Bureau of Standards, which is responsible for Federal Government standards, has said that it will use the IEEE standards when they are agreed.

DEC, INTEL AND XEROX CORPORATIONS – ETHERNET

The consortium of Digital Equipment Corporation, Intel Corporation, and Xerox Corporation for the development of Ethernet as an industry standard local area networking technique has been discussed elsewhere. It is interesting that a minicomputer manufacturer, a microelectronics chip manufacturer and an office products supplier should agree to co-operate on a single networking technique. It demonstrates the wide applicability of Ethernet.

Ethernet is very similar, but not identical (although it can be made to be the same if necessary), to the proposed IEEE CSMA/CD standard for a baseband coaxial cable network operating at 10 Mbps. Ethernet is fully specified up to and including the Data Link Layer, and a full unique addressing scheme has been devised for it – described elsewhere.

Where the IEEE work makes provision for different classes of service, such as datagram or sequenced with flow control, Ethernet is basically a datagram system.

Since it is so similar to the IEEE CSMA/CD proposal, Ethernet will not be described in detail again. As the IEEE work has progressed so Ethernet has been modified to be compatible but not identical. There seems little doubt that once the IEEE work reaches the stage of being a standard, then Ethernet will be brought into line, provided this does not conflict with the unique addressing scheme inherent in Ethernet and its 48-bit address fields.

Intel are actively working on the electronic chips which will be used to provide the normal transceiver interface to the network. Once these are available and in volume production, the cost of constructing Ethernet systems will decrease so much that the technique will become very popular. As it is, a large number of Ethernet licences have already been issued; enough to ensure that Ethernet will dominate the available products in the near future and so become a de facto standard.

PROWAY

Work on standardising Proway has been going on for longer than any other local networking technique. Its aim is rather different from the other standards discussed above. Proway is designed explicitly for process control systems with real-time control requirements and guaranteed access to the network. To meet these demands, the following set of requirements has been drawn up:

— *Reliability*

A Proway network should not cease to operate if any single device on that network fails in any way. The attached devices should always be able to use the network, so additional interface devices and duplicated media can be used.

— *Real-time*

Certain high-priority users must be able to gain access to the medium within around 2 ms.

— *Flow control*

Each device on the network has prior knowledge of all the other devices with which it is allowed to communicate.

— *Classes of data transfer*

Three classes of service are defined: datagram (in which no acknowledgement is required); message transfer (a non-time-critical acknowledgement is needed); and transaction (a non-interruptible transfer of a request/response pair between end-users).

The work on Proway is being considered by ISO, but not as a serious contender with the IEEE work nor Ethernet. It is aimed at such a different set of requirements from the normal local area network that they cannot be sensibly compared. Nor do the local area networking techniques under consideration by IEEE really meet the requirements served by Proway. It seems possible that, at this stage, standardisation of Proway may be held up until further work on the IEEE Token access technique has been completed to see if this will be suitable as an alternative.

CONCLUSIONS

Without doubt the most important effort in local area network standardisation is coming from the IEEE in the US. If this continues without
serious hitches, standards for the physical media, access techniques and
data link protocols should be published before the end of 1982. These will
cover the limited set of facilities provided by baseband coaxial cable
operating at speeds between 1 and 20 Mbps using CSMA/CD and Token
passing bus configurations. Extension of Token passing to rings is a
simple task.

However, it can be argued that this level of standardisation is still not
what the user really wants. The user requirement is for a standard method
of using a local area network which is independent of the underlying
medium and access mechanism. The IEEE work does not approach this.
It can be argued that the standard user interface should have been defined
first so that the user would be able to use the many different techniques
already on the market, none of which are compatible with the IEEE
proposal for a standard.

One of the most critical areas for standardisation is the interface
between local and wide area networks (public networks in particular).
Some more effort needs to be put into this.

A universal problem with standards is testing whether or not a particular implementation conforms to the standard or not. Standards should be
published with a mechanism for testing, but generally this is omitted until
a later stage. This area in computing has only recently received the
attention it deserves.

In the discussions of local area network standards in this chapter no
mention has been made of the Cambridge Ring. The technique was
considered by the IEEE but it was demonstrated theoretically not to be as
efficient as the Token passing technique so it was abandoned in favour of
the latter method. It has been said that the Cambridge Ring is similar to
the Token passing technique described, but it remains to be seen whether
current Cambridge Rings on the market and the associated devices will be
modified if and when a Token passing ring standard is agreed. As it
stands, it seems very unlikely that the normal Cambridge Ring will ever
be a true international standard. The UK emphasis is more on the need
for a standard interface to *all* local area networks at a level above that
associated with the access method.

9 Choosing a Local Area Network

INTRODUCTION

Most of this book is concerned with explaining the different techniques which have been used to provide a local data communications network. This chapter approaches the problem from the side of the potential purchaser of such a network. He is less concerned with how long the packets are or how they will be delivered to their destination, than with the kind of application which can be used on the network. As things stand, however, the underlying network, its topology and the way it operates, have a profound effect on the quality of service offered to the end-user.

In principle, a network could be designed which would offer its users the type of service they require. This could be achieved by making the network capable of handling sufficient bandwidth to suit all present and future requirements, and by providing enough software and hardware to allow the user to interface to all other kinds of equipment and to provide all the services he requires. Obviously such a solution, however desirable, would be beyond the finances of most organisations, and a product of this type would not find many customers.

The problem to be solved is how to make a network which is cheap enough but which has a sufficient number of facilities to make it appeal to the average company wanting to install a local network. Unfortunately no single product available is suitable for all customers. In this chapter some of the things which must be considered when choosing a network will be discussed. At this stage in the development of local area networking only general guidelines can be given as there is too little solid user experience which can be used as the basis.

OPTIONS FOR LOCAL NETWORKS

Before deciding on the actual local area network to buy, the potential customer should examine the existing facilities for communications within the organisation and decide which of these are relevant.

Most organisations will have a private telephone network installed on each site, usually based on a private exchange. The network generally serves directly or indirectly every user on site and provides facilities for them to talk to each other and to other individuals outside through the use of the public telephone network. Some of these on-site networks are used to enable computer terminals to connect to a computer through the use of modems or acoustic couplers. Whilst these lines are being used in this manner they are unavailable for normal telephone conversations.

The quality of the network and the exchange, and the extent to which they are used for data communications, are very important factors to take into account when considering how a local area network will be used. For example, if the existing private telephone exchange is due for replacement, the opportunity will be there to install an advanced digital PABX which will have facilities designed particularly for data communications between computer-related devices. Even the installation of new telephone wiring provides opportunities for the inclusion of extra cables which could ultimately be used for a local area network. The cost of putting in the wiring is considerably more than the cost of the wire. Even if the organisation was not actively considering installing a local area network when the time comes to upgrade the system, then it should do so at that stage. A few days employed on studying the data communications requirements could save the frustration and cost of installing a network which will be useless for data in a few years' time.

Networks which provide terminal users with facilities to access the on-site computer systems are usually installed in a piecemeal fashion. When a department or office requires a new terminal then a fresh set of cables are usually installed. Even where cables usually exist it is not uncommon for them to be ignored, either because no-one knows of their existence or because they are the wrong type, or even because no-one is sure why they are there or where they should go.

New terminals are now being installed so quickly that a better scheme needs to be devised for linking them into the computer system. The telephone network, since it is there, may be suitable, provided that the exchange can handle the traffic, and provided that the terminals are suitable for operation over this type of link. The solution which appeals to most users is the once-and-for-all installation of a local area network which can be used to link all computer-based devices.

In addition to these electrical information transfer facilities there is always the internal manual postal system to be considered. A study of this can be very enlightening for the designer of a local area network, especially where it is intended to serve as the basis of an electronic office system. Knowing the traffic patterns of the messages, how many stay wholly on the site and how many are external post, is essential information for the designer of an electronic mail system. In organisations with separate sites, the amount of post, and its character (eg letters, drawings, parcels, etc), passing between sites needs to be known, and whether the quantity justifies the existence of an inter-site electronic message system, or whether the computer network (if there is one) can be used instead.

Another aspect of the local communications problem is the need or desirability to integrate voice with data handling. Does the organisation want to install, for example, a text handling system with voice annotation? Is the provision of an electronic mail facility going to noticeably affect the use of the internal telephone system? Can incoming calls be stored on computer systems if the intended recipient is unavailable, or do sufficiently good arrangements already exist to take in-coming calls? All these factors need very careful consideration. Whatever conclusions are reached it must be recognised that the rates at which voice and data handling facilities will be expanded in the future are almost certain to be different. Any solution must be flexible enough to handle this.

As new items of equipment come onto the market, the need for extra communications facilities is certain to increase. Not only will the total quantity of information being moved around increase but the individual bandwidths required for new services could well be much greater than those of ordinary computer terminals. Take, for example, the 6 MHz bandwidth required for a one-way transmission of real-time colour television. This is sufficient for hundreds of conventional computer terminals. Broadband networks are the only really suitable systems available today to handle this quantity of information.

Summarising, the networking needs can be satisfied by using circuit, message or packet switched centrally controlled systems, local area networks using rings or buses, or by broadband systems. The last option has the greatest potential to handle all the on-site communications needs, but at greater cost than some other possibilities. The problems of the customer are often compounded by the limited choice of systems available which actually fulfil his complete requirements. One topic for consideration, therefore, is the relative urgency of the requirements. It may be advisable to wait until more products are on the market which are better oriented to the user's true needs.

USER EXPERIENCES

It is not surprising to learn that very few local area networks have yet been installed in ordinary working situations. Most installations have been in the research and development establishments, where most current technologies were developed, and more recently in company and educational establishments as pilot schemes. Like the research establishments, which were covered in detail in an earlier chapter, the situations for which local area networks have been used have been either as the interconnection medium for distributed computing networks, or as experimental electronic office schemes. There is no other reason, other than natural caution, why the same local network could not be used for both computing (in the traditional sense) networks and office automation, since many of the aims of the two, and much of the equipment used, are the same.

Discussions with users of local area networks have shown that the underlying communications technology (ring or bus, CSMA or empty slot) does not matter to them at all provided that the network achieves its main purpose of transporting information quickly and without introducing errors. The situation is likely to change significantly when special demands are made on the network, such as voice conversations, visual information and facsimile. Some networking techniques are not as suitable as others for these requirements which demand a high bandwidth and guaranteed use of the system.

Most of the networks which serve computing systems are similar in concept. Their aim is to provide a wide range of users with access to a limited number of computer systems. The normal method, before local area networks were introduced, was to provide groups of users with terminals which were linked to a computer system. When another computer was introduced into the installation it was often from a different supplier and was programmed to provide a different set of services. For the users to access and use it, extra terminals were needed or the provision of a network switch which would be able to route messages from the terminals to the appropriate computer system. The technique of using the proprietary networking systems provided by some computer suppliers is only possible in situations where one make of computer is used, and even then some users found the solution too slow, inefficient or costly.

Local area networks provided, at first sight, an ideal solution to the problems. The main obstacle was to find a product which could be used. This has led to the installation of a variety of different local network products, almost all of which provide little more than the basic data transmission system. Onto this, interfaces had to be built. The interfaces used are microprocessor-based and perform two tasks. The first is to provide a method of interfacing to the particular device being attached to the network. This interface must be capable of operating at the correct speed and must be able to either buffer messages passing to and from the device or use the appropriate signalling protocol to stop and start it at the right times. The other task it must perform is to address and package up the data correctly for transport over the network to the other end. Figure 9.1 shows how this device is normally constructed. The Network Interface Unit, as it is normally called, can usually support more than one attached device within the same physical box. For each device the interface software will be specific but the network access software and hardware will be shared (since there is only one connection actually to the network).

Suppliers of networks are usually able to provide a limited number of interfaces to the more popular terminals and computer systems. Other types may require the customer to program the microprocessors in the Network Interface Units. In most of the installations serving this type of computer local area network in the UK, the customer departments have been willing and able to put in the programming effort where this has proved necessary, with the supplier providing any help required.

Most, but not all, of the local area networks installed in distributed computing systems in the UK have been based on the Cambridge Ring technology. At the time of writing, the only Cambridge Rings freely available on the market have been fairly basic and have required user effort to write the interface to the attached devices. As more experience is gained in their use, and as customers become more demanding, the number of tried and tested interfaces will increase.

The Joint Network Team of the Computer Board and Research Coun-

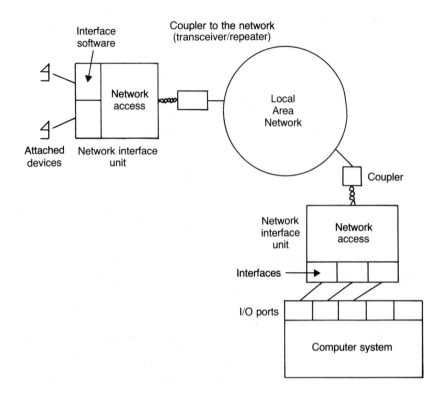

Figure 9.1   Interfacing to a Typical Network

cils is responsible for advising the computer services departments of universities in the UK on their networking requirements. Although their early work was on providing a network linking all the universities to provide access to university computer facilities from all over the UK, they become involved in on-site networks in an effort to encourage the use of a single standard technology. If this could be achieved, the problems of transferring data from one site to another, and of connecting together separate local networks belonging to different departments of the same university, would be reduced. A number of possibilities were examined once it was realised that some local networks had already been installed and were largely incompatible. Packet switched systems were included in the examination along with Cambridge Rings and Ethernet-based networks. It was felt that there was insufficient experience of using Ethernet systems within their particular type of general-purpose computing environment for any firm recommendation on their use to be made. Cambridge Rings, on the other hand, had been developed within the university environment to serve the same needs. Experiments on the use of X.25 packet switched networks had been conducted earlier.

The Joint Network Team decided to issue a set of requirements for a Cambridge Ring network which they felt would satisfy most of the needs of the computing services departments, although they knew that no such product was available. The requirements were put to tender to the main suppliers, most of whom were marketing only basic bit transfer networks. The networks required had to provide multiplexers, terminal concentrators and interfaces suitable for a range of small to medium-sized computer systems. In addition, a number of network services had to be provided: high-speed printing, error logging, name and address resolution with physical location on the network, and bridging between rings and to X.25 packet switched networks. Other facilities required included: ability to change device interfaces, alter the ring packet size, change the access logic, extend the topology of the network, freedom to move devices around without needing to change their network identifier, and ability to replace faulty equipment easily.

Although the above requirements were made specifically for Cambridge Ring systems for a particular class of network, they can easily be applied to any local network which is to support terminal access to computer systems.

Another group of users of local area networks have installed their system to serve the office environment and provide the cornerstone for an electronic office system. In the US, this type of network is dominated by Ethernet, since it was in just this situation that Ethernet was developed. In the UK, the same market has been dominated by the XINET and XIBUS systems developed by Xionics. Again, most of the installations have been experimental, because the techniques of local networking are new, and because the organisations involved have wanted to assess the effects on their staff of using computer-based equipment to aid some office procedures.

In the UK, five users of the Xionics system agreed to take part in pilot schemes. They were generally interested in providing word-processing and electronic mail facilities to their managerial and secretarial staff. Other facilities available included personal computing, text manipulation, personal filing and sharing files and large capacity storage devices. In general the experiments have shown that the office technology concepts are valid, although in the early stages certain operational problems were experienced with running a network which was essentially under continuous development and always being monitored.

PERFORMANCE

An exhaustive study of network performance is beyond the scope of this book and is still the subject of a considerable amount of research. Most of the practical work has been done on Ethernet systems (reference 9.1). Other work on performance has been largely theoretical. Reference 9.2 presents a review of much of the work. In this section the main things to look for are presented but it is impossible to make firm recommendations.

When considering network performance a number of constraints must be taken into account:

— *Inter-frame spacing*

After each frame transmitted on the network a gap is required to separate one frame from another. This gap may be filled with idle characters or frame preamble. Some characters are necessary before the actual frame proper starts in order that the receiver is allowed to synchronise with the signal. With the high speeds used on most local networks prior synchronisation is especially important.

— *Collision detection and reinforcement*

Contention-based systems (eg Ethernet) rely, for their successful operation, on the ability of the station to detect that a packet has been in collision with another, and then often they reinforce the collision by 'jamming' the network with a burst of characters. The total time occupied in this transmission, ie the part of the frame transmitted before the collision is detected plus the reinforcement characters, is time wasted.

— *Station reaction time*

Each device on the network needs a finite length of time to react to a transmission addressed to it. If this is long then the data which can be passed to that station is limited.

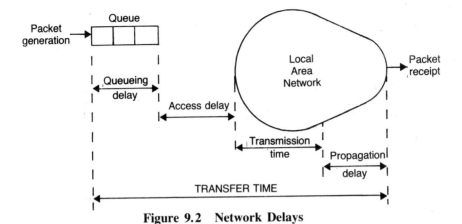

Figure 9.2   Network Delays

In considering the transfer of a packet of information from the source to its destination, the total time required is made up of (see Figure 9.2):

— *Queueing delay*

Once a packet is ready to send it must be queued in the interface device behind other packets also waiting to be sent.

— *Access delay*

A packet at the head of the queue cannot generally be transmitted immediately. It has to wait for a convenient gap in the network traffic or until that station is given permission to send.

— *Transmission time*

This is the time it takes to actually transmit the whole of the packet onto the network. It is governed by the speed of the network and the operating speed of the interface unit. Typically this will be in the region of 1-10 Mbps.

— *Propagation delay*

Each electrical impulse on the network travels at a high, but finite, speed (approximately three quarters of the speed of light) from the sender to the destination. Thus a small time has to be added for propagation onto the times already mentioned.

Once that packet reaches its destination it is subject to the station and device reaction times which are typically much longer than the propagation times. The time it takes a packet to pass across a network, however, is not predictable for every technique used. The main areas of doubt are in the queueing delay and the time to access the network. The former is important when the device generating the packets is capable of doing so at high speed, or when the network is congested. The latter time is governed by the network congestion and the transmission technique used. Other factors which affect the overall network performance are:

— *Stability*

> This is a measure of the time taken to successfully transmit a packet of information. If this approaches infinity under certain network operating conditions, the network is said to be unstable. Certain networking techniques are inherently more stable under all conditions than others.

— *Fairness*

> Fairness is the measure of the number of opportunities to transmit which each station has. If this is equal for every station then the network is fair. Fairness may not be a desirable characteristic in all circumstances. Some applications may require a limited number of stations to be always able to gain access to the network: one example is the control of a critical industrial system. Some networking techniques may be fair under normal circumstances but provision can be made for the user to allocate priorities, so that it can be made to operate in an 'unfair' manner, as far as the network is concerned, but in a more sensible manner from the user's point of view.

— *Robustness*

> Robustness of the network is a measure of how the network responds to failures of the media, attached devices or transceivers/repeaters. Related to this is the sensitivity or otherwise of the network whilst operating in an electrically noisy environment. This may be a very important point to consider in industrial systems in which the cable passes close to heavy machinery.

— *Failure modes*

The way a network fails can have important repercussions on the systems using it. If the failure of an attached device renders the whole network unusable this is unlikely to be acceptable to most users. Other failure modes which are acceptable would be an increase in delay or fewer opportunities to transmit.

— *Data transmission rate*

Although the raw data transmission rate of the network may appear to be one of the most important factors determining performance, an examination of Figure 9.2 will show that this is only a proportion of the total transfer time. Most current local area networks operate at a raw transmission rate of 10 Mbps. This is beyond the input/output capabilities of all but the larger computers, but even they still need time to frame outgoing data, and analyse incoming packets. A more typical end-point-to-end-point data transfer rate would be around 1 Mbps.

— *Variation in delays*

Experience of computer networks over many years has shown that quite considerable delays are acceptable provided they are nearly always the same. Variations between $\frac{1}{2}$ and 2 seconds, say, can be most annoying to a terminal user. In the networks which serve human users directly, variation in delay is an important factor.

— *Framing constraints*

The size of the packet which the network can transport affects, not only the size of the message which can be transported in one transmission, but also the size of the buffers required in the devices at each end.

To the above factors should be added the interaction needed between the network access mechanisms and the higher level protocols which must be used to provide the quality of service users and programs require.

Many of the analyses of network performance which have been published have not taken all the above factors into consideration. The authors of reference 9.3 criticise reference 9.1 for the extremely high figure obtained for Ethernet: 97%. In reference 9.1 the time required to process the packets, the time needed to access the network and buffer management are not taken into account in that 97%. Simulations have demonstrated that Ethernet performance is strongly dependent on these factors. Under special conditions certain networks perform in a different way from that which would happen under normal operating circumstances.

Generally Ethernet, the subject of reference 9.1, operates well at less than 50% loading with traffic coming in bursts from the attached devices. At higher loadings more collisions occur, with the result that more packets are damaged and have to be scheduled for retransmission. The average time to transmit a packet will increase, and at high loadings, accessing the network could be lengthy. Since the wait time before retrying to send a packet increases with the number of times that packet collides, a station which experiences problems can take much longer to successfully transmit than would a device which is just starting to transmit. Fairness in the Ethernet system is only experienced at low-to-medium loadings.

In contrast, both the ring empty slot and the bus or ring token passing methods are fair but they exhibit other performance deficiencies. For example, when the network is heavily loaded they will both be able to gain access within a time which is fairly predictable, but this time may be quite long. The token passing technique has the additional advantage that priority can be given to certain stations if their requirements dictate it.

The empty slot ring can also be modified to alter the 'fairness'. For example, in the normal ring the slot cannot be re-used immediately by the same station but must be emptied and passed on. By modifying the access method a slot can be retained by a station for as many revolutions of the ring as is desired. This has advantages for a station transmitting a long message which it has stored ready in a buffer. In practice most empty slot rings require that returning slots are examined to check that the destination has successfully received the information. The control field which indicates this must be at the end of the packet so the original sender has to read in all the packet before it knows whether the transmission was successful. Normally, therefore, the packet is not re-used immediately. If a packet is to be retained in use, other protocols at a higher level are needed to ensure that the message as a whole has been transmitted successfully.

In conclusion, network performance is a subject for a considerable amount of further research, not just involving theoretical calculations based on a 'typical' network traffic, but under real conditions. The user's perception of the service provided is still the most important factor. Work needs to be done on the more human aspects of performance: ie the delays and the variations which are acceptable.

INSTALLING THE NETWORK

The earlier parts of this book have shown that local area network technology and developments are currently in a very fluid state. It is difficult at this stage to make any quantitative judgement concerning network quality and performance, especially with so few experienced users in the UK. As more and more products come onto the market, and as the needs of the customer become clearer, we will see a more definite set of requirements emerge which will make it easier in many respects to choose a network.

At this stage the experience obtained in the other fields of computing and communications must be used when evaluating the requirements for a local area network. It is reasonably safe to assume that where the network is being installed to handle the same sort of communications as a more traditional network then the same criteria for evaluation can be used. But local area networks are probably going to be most commonly installed for new services based on the electronic office and the use of personal computers and intelligent workstations in the managerial and professional environments. We have no experience in the use of communications in these areas and hence it is not valid to use the same criteria that were developed for computer networks and distributed computing systems. The whole topic of computer-based office networks is still the subject of much research.

Probably the fullest account to date which covers designing, choosing and evaluating local area networks, with particular reference to their use in the office environment, was commissioned by the US National Bureau of Standards (NBS) – reference 9.4. The report is biased towards helping US Federal Agencies to choose a suitable local area network to meet their immediate needs. It does not consider in any detail the kind of products which are found mainly in the UK (eg systems based on the Cambridge Ring). It can be considered as a very good starting point for anyone seriously thinking of buying a local area network product. The report is split into four main sections:

(1) A review of existing local area network technologies;

(2) Determining the requirements of the installation;

(3) Preparing a statement of these requirements in the correct form for the US Government Agency, and for ultimately passing to the suppliers of the networks as specifications;

(4) Evaluating the technical proposals produced by the suppliers against the selection criteria of the appropriate customer.

On the whole, the report is very thorough, but it is very strongly oriented towards the standard procurement procedures employed by the US Government. For the purposes of this book the following procedures are recommended (although it is worth repeating that future research will expand them into a more useful set):

(1) Decide on the needs of the installation;

(2) Prepare a list of network features corresponding to the needs;

(3) Match the features required against the available products and decide which will be most suitable.

The remainder of this section is devoted to further consideration of these topics.

Customer Requirements

The first and most important aspect for consideration when planning to install a local area network is the purpose for which it will be used. Is it intended as the basis for an office automation scheme, a management, secretarial and professional system, a distributed computing network, a terminal network to a centralised computing system, or to interconnect the existing devices on the site? The services required for each of these systems are likely to be very different.

Office Technology

An office automation scheme will need a sophisticated filing system with the provision of a filestore or database which is accessible to all the users of the scheme. In most office schemes, some sort of text-handling and word-processing facilities will be required, and this could have a significant impact on the capabilities of the devices which can be used. Word-processing and other text-handling tasks really need special workstations with adequate editing and line manipulation facilities, otherwise they become tiring to use. Office automation and management, secretarial and professional systems also need electronic messaging, personal filing and many other facilities to be most effective. Finding all these on one local area network based system could be difficult, especially if that network is intended to be used for other tasks and the customer wishes to use it with a wide variety of devices from several suppliers.

Existing Equipment

In most instances the existing equipment on the site will have to be taken into account. In particular, equipment which is based on, or used with, computers should be considered as being potentially suitable for use on the network.

If the network is being designed to serve the existing computers and their terminals on the site, the number, type and location of them all must be established. It should also be decided which terminals normally work with which computers and whether this situation will continue once a network exists which can provide virtually unlimited interconnection between the devices which use it. If the computers are from different manufacturers then it is most unlikely that one will be able to interwork with another without the provision of special software and possibly hardware. Even the terminals from one supplier are unlikely to be suitable when used with another make of machine. If free interconnection between devices is required, and several types of device are currently installed, the local area network will need to have the appropriate interfaces and emulators to handle the different characteristics.

Alongside the consideration of the existing computer system, the future requirements and present state of the internal telephone system should be determined. If the internal telephone exchange is due for replacement then an advanced digital system may provide many of the internal data communications requirements at the same time as improving the telephone service.

Many organisations have been installing word-processor systems of various kinds over the past few years. The installation of a local area network provides the opportunity to improve the service offered, both to the typists and to the other members of staff who use the typing facilities.

Special Requirements

Some sites have problems which may affect the choice of the local network. For example, some sites are too large to be covered by some current local area networks. Even where the local networking technology does not limit the area to below that required, the efficiency or the cost may make it more sensible to split the site into two parts for the purposes of the network. However, the amount of traffic which is to pass between the two parts will influence the choice of network since some provide much better inter-networking facilities than others.

Many industrial sites are ideal candidates for using local area networks to interconnect the process control and monitoring equipment. These sites typically employ heavy electrical machinery which can seriously affect the transmission on some local networks. The cost of such a network can increase enormously if the cables have to be specially screened and passed through conduits or by circuitous routes past the offending machinery.

Traffic Flows

The other major topic to be taken into consideration in the early stages of planning the network is the quantity and direction of the expected traffic flows. If it is an existing network which is being updated or enhanced then fairly reasonable estimates of the traffic can often be made. Major problems arise, however, when the network is being designed to serve a new application.

Not only is the quantity of traffic to be handled a major consideration when designing a network, but also the main sources and destinations, and the identification of the nodes which create the majority of traffic, should be taken into account. All networks have to be designed to carry the peak traffic. Being sized for average traffic handling is not enough so the times when the major users of the network are involved in information exchange have to be estimated, together with the normal variations in the use. If the network is heavily loaded during any period then this could drastically affect the quality of service during that time. Not only will terminal and workstation users not get the response they are accustomed to, but the heavier users, such as computers and file servers, will find that sending or receiving information takes longer than it should, at the same time taking up computer resources which could be used for other purposes.

Although difficult to account for in the planning stages, the designer should realise that electronic office systems can change the patterns of use. This is treated in more detail in reference 9.5.

Performance and Monitoring

In order to understand how a network is performing once it is installed, it is necessary to have a monitoring device, or the appropriate software and hardware incorporated in an existing machine. Monitoring performance is often relegated to a secondary issue which is only thought of after the network (or any other system) is installed and it becomes evident that things are not working as well as they should. The need for monitoring, and the parameters to be monitored, should be recognised when the network is being designed. The role of the monitor in local area networks is rather different from that in other networks. Most experience of local networks has shown that a generally much lower data transmission error rate should be expected, line failures are very low, the bandwidth available is usually well in excess of requirements, and use of the network is not charged to the end-users. Thus the monitor should be concerned with ensuring that the network performs as expected, that any defective components or attached devices are located, and provide the necessary statistics to ensure that sensible decisions about developments can be made.

Because of the very high data transmission rates normally employed, a monitor of a local area network will find it difficult to read, analyse and store information about all the messages in transit. Some sort of filtering technique should be employed to analyse properly a selection of the traffic on the network. Background storage and processing facilities are essential if the monitor is to do this properly. The monitor should also be able to exist on the network without disturbing the system or the information flow. Certain systems are ideally suited to monitors; others less so. If possible, a monitor device can use quiet periods to send out special error detecting messages. Again, some local area networking systems do this as a matter of course (eg most Cambridge Rings); others do not.

Monitors can tell the customer how reliable the network is, but just as important to the user is the resilience. For example, what happens when an attached device is not working, or what is the effect when a repeater or transceiver fails in such a way that it continuously broadcasts information? The dependence, or otherwise, of the operation of the network as a whole on each of the individual components can be critical. From the user's point of view, how important is it to him that the network is always operational, and for how long can it cease to operate before it significantly affects his work? All these topics must be addressed before sensible decisions on the final network can be made.

Expandability

Almost every computer system and network which has been installed has proved inadequate for the job within a relatively short time. This fact should be recognised when a local area network is being considered, in spite of its apparently unlimited bandwidth. As far as possible, the need for expansion should be anticipated and a network chosen to fulfil, not only the present requirements, but those anticipated in the future as well. Since local area networks will frequently be installed to service the office automation environment, the extra capacity which may be required will be very difficult to estimate. Not only will the network be used to serve a relatively new area of use, but also the existing patterns of work in the office may change significantly. A network with flexibility in its topology and mode of use will be most valuable in a changing situation such as this.

Integrated Services

One area which will undoubtedly be important in the office environment in the near future is the integration of data with voice, facsimile and possibly other forms of information. Organisations should seriously consider the advantages of annotating text (reports, drafts, etc) with recorded voice messages. Not only does it make the task of commenting on and replying to messages much easier for the recipient, but it also allows much fuller information to be given. Voice, in the form of recorded messages, is fairly easy to incorporate in existing local area network technologies, but voice conversations are far more demanding. Real-time television pictures also place considerable demands on bandwidth. In some applications, real-time pictures need to be handled but it is often better to use the local area network for other purposes rather than take up all its bandwidth for video. The latest developments in broadband networks go a long way towards handling data and television on the same network, but even then the number of television channels which can be operated simultaneously is limited.

Extra Software Needed

Having decided what applications and devices are going to be put on the network, the customer should decide whether extra software will be needed to handle high-level protocols, file transfers, protocol emulation, etc. Almost certainly, unless the area of use is strictly limited, no one local area network system will be able to provide off-the-shelf all the facilities the user requires. The customers should, therefore, determine how much software for these purposes they can write themselves, and the minimum amount they will need to set up the system at the start.

Costs

Once all these factors have been taken into account, the cost of the installation can be estimated. It would be naive to suppose that a local area network will be as cheap as the wire needed to string the devices together. Even installations which have started with the basic transmission medium, and the minimum set of interfaces to it, have found that considerable effort is still required on their side to get it all to work together. The more sophisticated the network is, the more it will cost to buy; the more basic it is, the more time it takes to get it working in a useful manner.

At the time of writing, prices are varying very rapidly, but in rough terms the cable costs vary from a few pence per metre for twisted-pair cable to several pounds per metre for high-quality coaxial cable.

Ethernet transceivers cost around £200-£400, depending on type and quantity, but to these must be connected controllers at several hundred pounds per attached device. Prices for other systems are similar.

Network Features

The previous section was concerned with the user's perception of the network and the facilities it offers. This will need to be translated into specific network features before the requirements can be matched against advertised network characteristics. In this section the major characteristics of local area networks will be listed, together with the items which are affected by them.

> *Medium.* This is the actual physical medium used to carry the information. It may be simple twisted-pair telephone cable, coaxial cable (which is more expensive – very high quality cable can be difficult to bend and install), or even fibre optic cable if the desire is for long distances and high bandwidth. Some media are subject to electrical interference (eg twisted-pairs) and others are better

for long distances (eg coaxial or fibre optic cable). More important from practically every point of view is the way the medium is used.

Transmission Method. By transmission method we mean the signalling technique (baseband or broadband) and the technique for accessing and using the physical medium. Carrier sensed contention networks (CSMA/CD) and token passing are typical examples of the latter. The advantages and problems with each of the techniques have been discussed in detail in earlier chapters so they will not be re-iterated here. It is safe to say that no one technique is wholly suitable for all circumstances. Baseband CSMA/CD, despite its widespread use, has a limited bandwidth, can react badly when the network is heavily loaded, and is unsuitable for long distances and some continuous forms of traffic. Other techniques may be more expensive, too slow, or difficult to implement successfully, and yet be more suitable for some critical forms of traffic.

Topology. The actual shape of the network is probably less important than most other factors. It is not usually more difficult to install a ring than a bus, and the easier method of accessing and using a ring may outweigh the extra cost in cabling which may result. More important in practice are the distances between nodes (maximum and minimum) and the length of the network which is permitted. These can vary very considerably, even amongst networks using the same transmission technique.

Data transmission rate. Most suppliers of local area networks quote the basic data transfer rate of the network, usually between 1 and 10 Mbps. In practice, if two systems are exchanging information and they are sharing the network with others, then the data transfer rate between them will be considerably less. This, however, is the data rate which interests the end-user. It depends on the raw transmission rate, the access time, the time to analyse the information packets and the opportunities available to use the network. Customers should get justifiable quotations for point-to-point transmissions under specific operating conditions.

Addressing. Users of the network should be able to address other users by name rather than physical location on the network. If a user moves, this should not affect his network address. If more than one local area network is installed in an organisation or on a single site, problems may arise in addressing a user on another network. Some systems (eg Ethernet) allow for this by allocating world-wide unique addresses to every device. The penalty is a large overhead in the addressing fields of the information packets. In other systems the addressing is unique only within a network.

Error handling. The usual local area network provides simple facilities to detect and correct errors in transmissions between devices. Some provide higher-level facilities to handle lost packets, out of order packets and retransmissions. The needs of the customer vary probably more than the number of networks so the customer should ensure that the network under consideration has sufficient facilities to suit his own particular requirements.

Standards. Until standards at some agreed level have been set, the best that a customer can hope for is that the network uses a well-known technique. The number of other network products using the same technique is a rough measure of its acceptability. It seems fairly certain, however, that the first standards to appear will be for CSMA/CD and token passing on a bus.

Availability. It is annoying to go to the trouble of choosing a system which matches the requirements only to find that the supplier will not be able to provide it for some considerable time, and even then it may be different from that described in the earlier publicity literature. The availability of the system as described, and the enhancements being developed, should be ascertained early in the selection process.

Transmission facilities. In theory most local area networks allow information packets to be sent individually, and interspersed with others, from any one sender to all the other nodes on the network. In practice the situation may be very different. Frequently the interface devices set up a liaison or virtual circuit between the two end-points and during the time that liaison exists each end-point is restrained from receiving data packets from anywhere else. This may be acceptable for terminal use but for intelligent devices and professional workstations in an electronic office system it may be too restrictive. The problem may be easy to overcome by re-programming the network interface devices, although the customers may have to do this themselves. Also useful for some systems is the ability to broadcast a single message to everybody or the whole of a group.

Supplier's reputation. Some of the suppliers of local networks are new-comers to computer communications and hence may not be very well known. In fact some of the companies have only been in existence for a few months. Most customers do not just buy a product and then forget about it. They want to be assured that when something goes wrong the supplier will be able to put it right. Also important to many potential customers is the existence of some other installations. It is much more assuring to see someone else with a system then to just read about it in a brochure.

Services offered. Most customers of a network will want more than the basic transmission system. They will want a set of services such as monitoring, file storage, communications gateways to public networks, etc. The services required can be determined only by the customer himself. Generally those wishing to use their network in the office environment will want a wider range of services than will the customers just looking for an easy way to interconnect their computers and terminals.

Choosing the Network

Having gone through the exercise outlined in the two preceding sections, most potential customers will, at the present time, find that choosing a network will not pose a very difficult problem. There are so few products on the market that it will be difficult to find more than one with the required set of facilities. In fact there are too few products with a wide range of features for a true comparison to be made.

Local area networks can be supplied as part of a package, put together by a single manufacturer to serve a particular set of requirements. Some office automation systems come in this form, but generally provide very few facilities for connecting to larger computer systems. Suppliers of local area networks designed around computer systems generally assume that all the services needed will be provided as application programs on the computer itself and seldom take into account that customers may wish to use personal computers or office workstations with them.

Buying a local area network as part of a package brings with it the old problem of using proprietary systems: will the customer be 'locked' into using equipment from a single supplier, which does not necessarily provide him with the flexibility he requires, nor all the benefits which a distributed system can offer? Buying a network from a completely independent supplier brings another set of problems. For instance, how many different types of device can be used with the system, is the supplier going to provide new interfaces to suit the devices the customer wants to use, etc?

A welcome innovation in the field of computing has been introduced by some suppliers of local area networks. That is the provision of a trial system consisting of a limited number of interfaces and interconnecting cable, but sufficient for an undecided customer to try out a local network in his own environment. It takes the form of a pilot scheme, and as such must be treated as most other pilot systems. The customer must realise that the pilot system will not have the quantity nor type of traffic which will be typical of a full-scale system. Any simulation of traffic will still not be typical since a limited number of stations will be involved.

Some large organisations have taken the view that since local area networks are relatively cheap, and since there are likely to be several installed in the organisation during the next few years, it will be worth their while installing a proper pilot network within one department which will be used in the manner which will become the norm for other departments. The pilot network is often used for distributed computing, by replacing the existing point-to-point network of wires interconnecting computers and terminals, or it is used in the electronic office system in which a significant proportion of the members of the department have workstations on their desks and on which they perform some of their usual office tasks. Only by these methods can the full potential of local area networking be properly analysed. Further work in this area should be oriented towards bringing the experiences of these pilot schemes to a wider public.

CONCLUSIONS

It is really too early in the development and marketing cycle of local area networks for many definite guidelines to be deduced. Indeed, it is not obvious yet what facilities, services, applications, etc, envisaged for them will stand the test of time, especially in the field of office technology.

Distributed computing was hailed during the mid-1970s as being the ideal solution to many of the computing problems of the day, but products suitable to all classes of user were slow to come onto the market, and many mainframe computer manufacturers were reluctant to give up the idea of a central system controlling everything. In the meantime the power of the terminal has increased enormously by the addition of microprocessors. Now terminals are often known as workstations and are quite capable of performing many basic text and file handling functions on their own without reference to a mainframe computer. The arguments in favour of distributed computing are still largely valid, but no longer are we talking about a computer per office or factory or department but instead it is a computer per person.

A computer on every desk is all very well, but connected together in a network so that expensive resources and files can be shared, and also being able to exchange information easily, makes a lot of economic sense. Local area networks are just another shared resource, but one which enhances the complete system.

That is the stage we have reached now. What new applications will be found for networks each with so many computers, and with their costs and that of storage still falling so rapidly, only time will tell, but distributed computing of this form is here to stay.

10 The Future

INTRODUCTION

There can be little doubt that local area networks are going to be installed in vast numbers in the next few years, since they offer a very convenient method of providing on-site communications for both the data processing and office technology networks. Conventional data processing systems usually rely on a large computer to do large quantities of processing on large quantities of data held on files or a database at that location. Some distributed systems benefit from holding some information in a limited number of sites which are conveniently placed to minimise the amount of traffic required on the network. Local area networks are unlikely to alter the pattern of working on these systems, at least in the near future.

In the office the situation is different because the computer has, until now, made relatively little impact on the information handling tasks performed by every office worker. The mainframe system was never used to handle the manager's in- and out-trays, and very seldom did it provide the secretary with diary or word-processing facilities. The introduction of the workstation with its powerful in-built processing power and its ability to communicate with other workstations and computer systems via the local area network is going to alter office procedures very drastically. Although the technology is here now, is the work-force ready for the change, and will management be able to adapt to new techniques?

In France the potential of the use of computer technology in the office was recognised some years ago and a research scheme was initiated to examine all aspects of it. This is the KAYAK project and is briefly described in the next section as it indicates the sort of facilities which are likely to be typical in the future. In the remainder of the chapter the implications, market and future developments of local area networks are discussed.

KAYAK

The KAYAK pilot study into office technology was started in 1979 at the Institut National de Recherche en Informatique et en Automatique (INRIA) (reference 10.1). The project set out to examine possible local area networking infrastructures, a special multipurpose workstation and a number of services for use in the office. The common workstation is also used as the means to access larger computer resources and special-purpose server devices (database, communications gateways, etc).

In order to examine local area networking, two different types of network were implemented. One is called TARO and is a token passing ring using twisted-pair cable and operating at 50 kHz. The other is a contention bus using coaxial cable, 1 km long and operating at 1 Mbps. The contention algorithm used is CSMA/CD. Both networks operate satisfactorily and have a set of high-level protocols built on them. They are able to offer point-to-point sessions, datagram or broadcast services to their users.

The multipurpose workstation, BUROVISEUR, is a very advanced example of an office workstation. It can be adapted to the requirements of the user and has advanced screen formatting facilities so that parts of the screen may be used for different activities in parallel. For example, the user can display the contents of his electronic in-tray and a list of people to telephone at the same time. The workstation is intended to be easy to use.

The services provided on KAYAK include AGORA, an electronic messaging and mail handling system, and PLUME, an advanced editing system. PLUME can handle not only text files but also drawing, facsimile and voice, in a limited manner.

KAYAK has shown what can be done by applying the technologies of microprocessing and local area networking to the normal office proce-dures. The aim is to integrate the office functions of information pro-duction, filing, distribution and processing into one system. Each of the services implemented has been built up using these basic functions.

THE MARKET FOR LOCAL NETWORKS

Over the next few years it is certain that more and more computer-based devices will be bought, not only by the normal purchasers of computer equipment, the large company, but also by the small user.

The large user has been well grounded in the use of computers and is fully aware of the limitations of computing and the kind of inefficiencies which can creep in to the system. The newcomer is likely to make mistakes but since the new equipment is cheap, compared with the longer-established computers, the mistakes will not be too costly. Interconnecting these personal computers, workstations and small machines is likely to bring many benefits, provided the means to transmit information is cheap and the application programs needed by the small user are readily available.

Both of these classes of user will be customers for local area networks. Local networks should combine the characteristics of cheapness and wide applicability so that the same technology can be used for interconnecting a few personal microcomputers, interconnecting computers and terminals in a distributed system, or for an office automation scheme with a large number of intelligent workstations and few, if any, large computer systems.

Do current local area networks match up to these requirements? Unfortunately the answer is no. To be of value to the small user, local area network vendors need to provide a set of application packages for accounting, filing, stock control, etc. Some of these can be obtained for specific microcomputer systems but not generally to work in a network. Other classes of user of local networks want a system which provides network services, electronic messaging, protocol conversions to other computers, and ease of use, without the need for enormous quantities of extra programming. Local area network products do not provide many facilities of this character yet.

It appears that the suppliers of the network are going to be driven strongly by the needs of the users, which is how it should be. Users must make their feelings known to the suppliers otherwise the networks which come onto the market will lack the functions needed.

DEVELOPMENTS

The techniques used in local area networks are being developed continuously as a result of the experience gained in implementing and using them in real working situations. Not long ago very few local networks operated at much over 1 Mbps, but now the norm in around 10 Mbps. The limit is usually set by a balance between an adequate transmission rate and the cost of implementing it. The HYPERchannel system has been available for some time and it uses up to four trunk channels each capable of handling 50 Mbps, giving a total network bandwidth of 200 Mbps. Few, if any, installations actually use all of this but it does demonstrate that 10 Mbps is still well within what is possible. The problem about using a very high data rate is in designing the interface devices which lie between the physical medium and the attached device. For example, HYPER-channel's interface units are very expensive when compared with the costs of a typical office workstation or even a minicomputer, but very high data rates can be supported. By restricting the network to 10 Mbps the interface hardware is greatly simplified, so much so that most of the interface functions can be implemented on a single LSI chip. In view of this it is likely that the baseband networks aimed at the 'mass market' will use 10 Mbps for the basic transmission speed for some time to come.

The other technical area where major developments are taking place is in broadband networks where several channels exist in parallel on a single CATV coaxial cable network. As explained in earlier chapters the technique uses radio frequency transmissions with the information modulated onto the carriers by RF modems. The technique has been in use for many years but a major advantage came when someone decided to share a single channel amongst several users using time division multiplexing. Current implementations of local area networking using broadband transmission usually employ a small number of channels, each of which is shared by several users using bus contention principles. Alongside these shared channels a number of dedicated point-to-point channels are used for connecting devices with requirements for large quantities of data transmission.

The next development is going to be the incorporation of switching into the network so that point-to-point channels can be created and destroyed as and when necessary by the end-users. The problem yet to be solved satisfactorily is the use of telephones on a broadband network. Since it is essential to have a radio frequency modem between the network and the attached device, it is unrealistic to use ordinary telephones on such a network. The cost of the modem is many times greater than the cost of the telephone.

Some standards pertinent to local area networks are slowly emerging, some of which are based on existing products and systems. However, the standards are IEEE standards and not fully international ones. The latter will take much longer to be agreed. Work has begun at the international level on enhancing the open systems interconnection networks. Judging by past experience, useful agreed standards may take anything between three and five years. In the meantime many products will come onto the market conforming to a greater, or more likely, a lesser degree to the final standard. One existing supplier of a local area network has published the statement that they do not see that the forthcoming IEEE standards will have any impact on their system. They intend to sell sufficient numbers so that their network will become a de facto standard! In other words we will have a number of different designs on the market all claiming to be de facto standards. This is precisely the situation which happened with normal computer systems, their terminals and peripherals. Users are still suffering the consequences. Let us hope more sense will prevail this time and the suppliers will see the advantages to them as well as to their customers in using a standard which is accepted throughout the industry.

References

CHAPTER 1

1.1   IEEE Computer Society, Local Area Networks Standards Committee, *Functional Requirements Document,* 1981.

1.2   Bleazard G B, *Why Packet Switching?,* NCC Publications, 1979

CHAPTER 2

2.1   Price S G, *Introducing the Electronic Office,* NCC Publications, 1979

CHAPTER 3

3.1   Lindsey W C and Simon M K, *Telecommunications Systems Engineering,* Prentice-Hall, 1973

3.2   Parsupathy S, Correlative Coding: A Bandwidth Efficient Signalling Scheme, *IEEE Transactions on Communications,* July 1977, pp 4 -11

CHAPTER 4

4.1   Davies D W, Barber D L A, Price W L and Solomonides C M, *Computer Networks and their Protocols,* John Wiley & Sons, 1979

4.2   Penney B K and Baghdadi A A, Survey of Communications Loop Networks, Parts 1 and 2, *Computer Communications,* Vol 2, Nos 4 and 5, August and October, 1979

CHAPTER 5

5.1   Metcalfe R M and Boggs D R, Ethernet: Distributed Packet Switching for Local Computer Networks, *Communications of the ACM,* Vol 19, No 7, July 1976

5.2   Digital Equipment, Intel and Xerox Corporations, *The Ethernet. A Local Area Network. Data Link Layer and Physical Layer Specifications,* Version 1.0, September 1980

5.3   Wilkes M V and Wheeler D J, *The Cambridge Digital Communications Ring,* Paper presented at local Area Communications Network Symposium, Boston MA, May 1979

5.4   Meisner N B, Willard D G and Hopkins G T, *Time Division Digital Bus Techniques Implemented on Coaxial Cable,* Computer Networking Symposium, National Bureau of Standards, Gaithersburg, MD, December 1977

CHAPTER 6

6.1   Digital Equipment, Intel and Xerox Corporations, *The Ethernet. A Local Area Network. Data Link Layer and Physical Layer Specifications,* Version 1.0, September 1980

6.2   Shoch J F, *Carrying Voice Traffic Through an Ethernet Local Network— A General Overview,* Xerox Corporation, August 1980

6.3   Hafner E R, Nenadal Z, Tschanz M, A Digital Loop Communication System, *IEEE Transactions on Communications,* June 1974, pp 877-881

CHAPTER 8

8.1   ISO, *Open Systems Interconnection— Basic Reference Model, Draft Proposal 7498,* August 1981

8.2   Gee K C E, *An Introduction to Open Systems Interconnection,* NCC Publications, 1980

8.3   IEEE Computer Society, Local Area Network Standards Committee, *Functional Requirements Document,* 1981

CHAPTER 9

9.1   Shoch J F and Hupp J A, *Measured Performance of an Ethernet Local Network*, Xerox Palo Alto Research Center, February 1980

9.2   Hayes J F, Local Distribution in Computer Communications, *IEEE Communications Magazine*, March 1981

9.3   Lissack T, Maglaris B and Chin H, Impact of Microprocessor Architectures on Performance of Local Network Interface Adaptors, *Local Networks and Distributed Office Systems*, Online Publications, 1981

9.4   National Bureau of Standards, *Guidelines for the Selection of Local Area Computer Networks*, Report No. ICST/LANP-81-5

9.5   Pritchard J A T and Wilson P A, *Planning Office Automation— Electronic Message Systems*, NCC Publications, 1982

CHAPTER 10

10.1   Naffah N, Distributed Office Systems in Practice, *Local Area Networks and Distributed Office Systems Conference*, Online Publications, 1981

Glossary

ANALOGUE TRANSMISSION
Transmission of a continuously varying signal.

APPLICATION
A job or task which can be performed using a computer system.

APPLICATION PROGRAM OR SOFTWARE
A set of computer instructions which are executed by the computer to perform some task directly associated with an application.

ARCHITECTURE
A framework for a computer or communications system which defines its functions, interfaces and procedures.

BANDWIDTH
The lower and upper frequencies which are available for transmission.

BASEBAND
Information is encoded directly onto the transmission medium. Only one information signal is present on the medium at any time.

BROADBAND
A method of using a transmission medium having a wide frequency bandwidth. In it several signals can be carried simultaneously by allocating different channels to separate frequency bands.

BROADCAST
All devices on the system (network or medium) are capable of receiving all signals transmitted by others.

CATV (Community Antenna Television)
The distribution of television signals from a central point by means of cables.

CCITT (COMITÉ CONSULTATIF INTERNATIONAL TÉLÉ-GRAPHIQUE ET TÉLÉPHONIQUE)
The international body through which the national telecommunications bodies coordinate their activities.

CIRCUIT SWITCHING
A method of connecting together two users of a transmission service which allocates a circuit for their exclusive use for the duration of the call.

CHANNEL
A means of transporting information signals. Several channels can share the same physical circuit.

COLLISION
When two information signals attempt to use the same channel simultaneously.

CONCENTRATION
The function of channelling information from a number of users onto a smaller number of higher-capacity links. A concentrator is the device which performs this function and it is generally programmable. (Compare with Multiplexing.)

CONNECTION
A circuit consisting of means for conveying information from one place to another.

CONTENTION
When more than one user attempts to use the same channel simultaneously.

CSMA (CARRIER SENSE MULTIPLE ACCESS)
A method of sharing a channel. Before transmitting any information, the sender looks for the presence of a carrier signal, indicating that the channel is already being used. If a carrier signal is not present, the sender can transmit.

DATABASE
An organised collection of information in which data is available to

all systems, instead of each specific application having its own individual collections.

DATAGRAM

A single packet, in a packet switched network, which is routed without reference by the network to any other datagram being sent.

DCE (DATA CIRCUIT-TERMINATING EQUIPMENT)

A CCITT term which denotes the equipment which terminates the PTT (qv) supplied circuit. A modem is an example.

DISTRIBUTED DATABASE

One organised collection of data which has been subdivided or copied, and distributed amongst several different locations in a distributed system.

DISTRIBUTED PROCESSING

The distribution of information processing functions amongst several different locations in a distributed system.

DISTRIBUTED SYSTEM

An information processing system in which a number of individual processors at different locations are linked together so that they can cooperate.

DTE (DATA TERMINAL EQUIPMENT)

A CCITT term which denotes the customer equipment which is connected to a DCE (qv). Computers and terminals are examples of DTEs.

END-USER

A person who uses an information processing system.

FILE

An organised collection of data records which can be accessed by name.

FILESTORE

A collection of files, residing at a particular system, including the names of the individual files and descriptions of their properties.

GATEWAY

A computer system or exchange in one network which allows access to and from another network.

HDLC (HIGH-LEVEL DATA LINK CONTROL)

A protocol designed for data transmission which does not use control characters and is data-independent.

HOST

A computer system on which applications can be executed and which also provides a service to users of a computer network.

INFORMATION PROCESSOR

A computer which provides computing, data storage and data manipulation services for end-user applications.

INTERFACE

A boundary between two devices or two pieces of software across which the form and functions of the signals which pass it are specified.

ISO (INTERNATIONAL ORGANIZATION FOR STANDARDIZATION)

The body which exists to promote the development of standards in the world. Membership consists of national organisations which are most representative of standardisation in their countries.

LAYER

A set of logically related functions which are grouped together. Interfaces to and from the layer can be standardised but not the ways the internal functions are performed.

LOGICAL CONNECTION

A connection in which the means of information transfer may not exist as a real physical entity for the duration of the call.

MANCHESTER ENCODING

A technique for sending information bit-serially, in which the data and clock signals are combined.

MESSAGE

A logically related collection of data to be moved.

MODEM

A piece of equipment which converts digital signals into analogue or varying electrical signals for transmission over normal telephone lines. The modem also performs the reverse function.

MULTIPLEXING

The use of a single physical link for two or more simultaneous separate transmissions. A *multiplexer* is the device which performs this function. It is not usually programmable by the user.

MULTI-POINT or MULTIDROP CONNECTION
A circuit which is connected to several different destinations.

NODE
A point at which two or more communications lines meet. Usually applied to a computer or switching device situated at this position.

OPEN SYSTEMS INTERCONNECTION
Standardised procedures for the exchange of information between terminals, computers, people, networks, etc, which are accessible to one another by virtue of their mutual use of these procedures.

PACKET
A block of data with a defined format containing control and data fields.

PACKET SWITCHING
A term used in a data transmission network which is designed to carry the data in the form of packets. The data, in packets, is passed to the network, and devices within it use the control information to transmit the packet to the correct destination.

PHYSICAL CONNECTION
A transmission means between two or more users which usually consists of electrical conductors along which signals are transmitted.

POLLING
A process whereby terminals are invited one at a time to transmit information.

PROTOCOL
A set of rules to ensure a meaningful communication between co-operating partners.

PTT (POST, TELEGRAPH AND TELEPHONE ADMINISTRATION)
A general term to denote a supplier of telecommunications services.

PUBLIC DATA NETWORK
A communications system which is intended for transmission of digital data, and which is available to anyone wishing to subscribe to it.

REAL-TIME
Normally used to describe the situation where a computer is used to control and monitor directly a manufacturing process.

REPEATER
A device used to regenerate, amplify and retransmit signals.

RESOURCE
A hardware or software component of a system which can serve a user requirement.

ROUTEING
The function of selecting the path for transmission of data within a network.

SATELLITE PROCESSOR
A computer system which has a subsidiary role in a distributed system.

SESSION
When two pieces of software, two users, resources, or other components in a network, are connected together for the purpose of exchanging information, they are said to be in session.

STATION
A single addressable unit on a network. A station may represent a single device or a group of devices attached through another (eg a concentrator).

SWITCHING
In computer or communications networks, switching is the process by which services or data are directed to the appropriate user.

SYSTEM
A collection of computers, associated software, peripherals, terminals, human users, etc, that form an autonomous whole capable of information processing.

TERMINAL
A device which allows an end-user to input data to and receive it from a computer system.

TRANSACTION PROCESSING
The entering of records of events into information processing systems as each event occurs.

TRANSCEIVER

A transmitter/receiver through which devices can access the network.

TRANSPARENT

A communications link is said to be transparent when it does not alter in any way the contents of the messages it transmits. A computer system or program used as an interface to another system is transparent when the user is aware only of the final system.

VIRTUAL CIRCUIT

A call using a virtual circuit uses real physical connections which the transmission service may employ for other calls made by other subscribers.

V-SERIES (CCITT)

The CCITT recommendations for data transmission over telephone (ie analogue) networks.

X-SERIES (CCITT)

The CCITT recommendations for data transmission over digital data networks.

Index